Bookkeeping Transactions

Workbook

David Cox
Michael Fardon

Published by Osborne Books Limited
Tel 01905 748071
Email books@osbornebooks.co.uk
Website www.osbornebooks.co.uk

Design by Laura Ingham

Printed by CPI Group (UK) Limited, Croydon, CR0 4YY, on environmentally friendly, acid-free paper from managed forests.

MIX
Paper from
responsible sources
FSC® C013604

British Library Cataloguing in Publication Data
A catalogue record for this book is available from the British Library

ISBN 978 1909173 668

Contents

Introduction

Chapter activities

Answers to chapter activities

Practice assessments – tasks

Answers to practice assessments

Also available from Osborne Books...

Tutorials

Clear, explanatory books written
precisely to the specifications

Wise Guides

Handy pocket-sized study and revision guides

Student Zone

Login to access your free ebooks and
interactive revision crosswords

Download **Osborne Books App** free from the App Store or Google Play Store
to view your ebooks online or offline on your mobile or tablet.

www.osbornebooks.co.uk

Introduction

Qualifications covered

This book has been written specifically to cover the Unit 'Bookkeeping Transactions' which is mandatory for the following qualifications:

AAT Foundation Certificate in Accounting – Level 2

AAT Foundation Diploma in Accounting and Business – Level 2

AAT Foundation Certificate in Bookkeeping – Level 2

AAT Foundation Certificate in Accounting at SCQF Level 5

This book contains Chapter Activities which provide extra practice material in addition to the activities included in the Osborne Books Tutorial text, and Practice Assessments to prepare the student for the computer based assessments. The latter are based directly on the structure, style and content of the sample assessment material provided by the AAT at www.aat.org.uk.

Suggested answers to the Chapter Activities and Practice Assessments are set out in this book.

Osborne Study and Revision Materials

The materials featured on the previous page are tailored to the needs of students studying this Unit and revising for the assessment. They include:

- **Tutorials:** paperback books with practice activities
- **Wise Guides:** pocket-sized spiral bound revision cards
- **Student Zone:** access to Osborne Books online resources
- **Osborne Books App:** Osborne Books ebooks for mobiles and tablets

Visit www.osbornebooks.co.uk for details of study and revision resources and access to online material.

Chapter activities

1   The accounting system

1.1   A sale for immediate settlement made at a shop using a bank debit card is known as a:

(a) Cash sale	
(b) Credit sale	
(c) Debit sale	

Tick the appropriate box.

1.2   An entry in a book of prime entry is:

(a) An entry in the ledger accounts of a business	
(b) An entry in the trial balance of a business	
(c) The first place an entry is recorded in the accounting records	

Tick the appropriate box.

1.3   The 'ledger' system of accounts is normally set up for recording:

(a) Cash transactions only	
(b) Cash and credit transactions only	
(c) Cash and credit and other financial transactions	

Tick the appropriate box.

1.4 A sales ledger control account contains the totals of accounts of:

(a) Customers who buy goods and services on a cash basis	
(b) Customers who buy goods and services on a credit basis	
(c) Suppliers who provide goods and services on a cash basis	
(d) Suppliers who provide goods and services on a credit basis	

Tick the appropriate box.

1.5 Select the missing words from the selection below to complete the following text:

A [ ] sets out in two columns the balances of the

[ ] of a business.

The [ ] of the two columns should [ ] . The debit column

includes the accounts of [ ] and the credit column includes the accounts of

[ ] . This provides the [ ] of a business with important and

useful financial information.

Choose from:

payables	**agree**	**ledger accounts**	**managers**
receivables	**totals**	**trial balance**	

2 Financial documents for sales

2.1   Praxis Stationery has supplied the following goods to a credit customer, Dover Designs.

The list price of the goods is £4.00 per box file, plus VAT at 20%. Dover Designs is to be given a 20% trade discount and a 2% prompt payment discount for settlement within 14 days.

DELIVERY NOTE   **No** 246
PRAXIS STATIONERY   **Date** 09 07 20-3
45 Jarvis Street
Mereford MR1 2GH

Dover Designs
68 Whitecliff Street, Granstow, GR3 7GH   Customer code DO109

---

100 Box files, Code BX100

(a)   **You are to** complete the following invoice:

INVOICE   **No** 1689
PRAXIS STATIONERY   **Date** 09 07 20-3
45 Jarvis Street
Mereford MR1 2GH
VAT Reg 831 8627 06

To
Dover Designs
68 Whitecliff Street, Granstow, GR3 7GH   Customer code

                                                 Delivery note no

Quantity	Product code	Unit price (£)	Total (£)	Net (£)	VAT (£)	Total (£)

(b) If Dover Designs decides to take advantage of the prompt payment discount it will take which **one** of the following actions:

(a) Reduce the amount of the invoice total by 2%	
(b) Request Praxis Stationery to issue a new invoice	
(c) Request a credit note for the amount of the discount (including VAT)	

Tick the appropriate box.

2.2 The following transactions have been passed through the account of a Rosetti Associates, a new credit customer of Praxis Limited:

Date	Document	Amount £
1 August	Invoice 1748	4,567.89
9 August	Invoice 1778	2,457.60
10 August	Invoice 1783	4,678.30
17 August	Credit note 319	280.50
29 August	Cheque	4,287.39

You are to complete the statement of account shown below:

STATEMENT OF ACCOUNT
PRAXIS STATIONERY
45 Jarvis Street, Mereford MR1 2GH

To Rosetti Associates
Date 31 08 20-3

Date	Details	Amount £	Balance outstanding £
1 August	Invoice 1748		
9 August	Invoice 1778		
10 August	Invoice 1783		
17 August	Credit note 319		
29 August	Cheque		

2.3 Praxis Limited codes all sales invoices with a customer code and a general ledger code.

A selection of the codes used is given below.

Customer	Customer Account Code
Artex Ltd	ART09
Bristol Wholesale	BRI25
Britmore Ltd	BRI45
Coleman Trading	COL10
Coldring Limited	COL12

Item	General Ledger Code
Paper products	GL4002
Pens	GL4003
Storage	GL4008
Printer inks	GL4017
Files	GL4018

Indicate in the table below the appropriate customer and general ledger codes that would be applied to the the following sales invoices:

Product	Customer	General Ledger Code	Customer Code
Copy paper	Britmore Ltd		
Gel pens	Coldring Limited		
Box files	Artex Limited		
Black printer ink	Coleman Trading		
Archive storage boxes	Bristol Wholesale		
Suspension files	Britmore Limited		

2.4 The financial document which is sent by the seller of goods or services and reduces the amount due to the seller is:

(a) A refund note	
(b) A debit note	
(c) A credit note	

Tick the appropriate box.

2.5 A business sells goods which have a list price of £800. The following discounts are available to the buyer:

- 20% trade discount
- 5% prompt payment discount for settlement within 14 days

(a) The sales invoice should show a VAT amount (at 20%) of:

(a) £121.60	
(b) £128.00	
(c) £160.00	

Tick the appropriate box.

(b) The total price for the goods on the invoice should be:

(a) £729.60	
(b) £768.00	
(c) £960.00	

Tick the appropriate box.

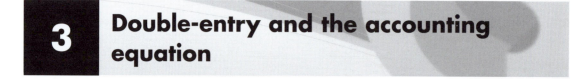

3 Double-entry and the accounting equation

3.1 Where does double-entry take place?

Select **one** option.

(a) In the trial balance	
(b) In the books of prime entry	
(c) In the ledgers	✓
(d) In the day books	

3.2 The ledger which contains the accounts of suppliers is the:

(a) Purchases ledger	
(b) General ledger	
(c) Sales ledger	

Which **one** of these options is correct?

3.3 The table below lists payments and receipts of a business which pass through the Bank Account. Write the names of the two accounts involved in the double-entry in the correct columns. The first entry is completed to show what is required. The name of the account which is not the Bank account is shown in bold type in the left-hand column.

	Debit	Credit
Money paid for **Purchases**	Purchases	Bank
Money received from **Sales**	Sales	
Rent paid for premises used		Rent
Rent received for premises let		
Motor expenses paid		
Payment for **advertising** costs		
Stationery bill paid		
Loan received	Loan	Bank
Loan repayment made		Loan

3.4 The Bank Account shown below has been written up by the bookkeeper, but the double-entry has not yet been done. Use the blank accounts set out on the next page by completing the account name, date details and amount for each entry.

Dr			Bank Account			Cr
2013		£		2013		£
1 Feb	Sales	5,000		1 Feb	Purchases	3,500
2 Feb	Sales	7,500		2 Feb	Wages	2,510
3 Feb	Bank Loan	12,500		3 Feb	Purchases	5,000
5 Feb	Sales	9,300		4 Feb	Rent paid	780

Debit			....Account		Credit
Date	Details	£	Date	Details	£

Debit			....Account		Credit
Date	Details	£	Date	Details	£

Debit			....Account		Credit
Date	Details	£	Date	Details	£

Debit			....Account		Credit
Date	Details	£	Date	Details	£

Debit			....Account		Credit
Date	Details	£	Date	Details	£

3.5 Financial accounting is based upon the accounting equation.

(a) Show whether the following statements are true or false.

Statement	True	False
(a) Liabilities equals capital plus assets		
(b) Assets equals liabilities minus capital		
(c) Capital equals assets minus liabilities		

(b) Classify each of the following items as an asset or a liability.

Item	Asset	Liability
(a) Vehicles		
(b) Bank loan		
(c) Money owing by trade receivables		
(d) Inventory		
(e) Cash		
(f) VAT owing to HM Revenue & Customs		

3.6 Fill in the missing figures:

Assets	Liabilities	Capital
£	£	£
50,000	0	....
40,000	10,000	....
55,200	....	30,250
....	18,220	40,760
40,320	15,980	....
....	24,760	48,590

3.7 An increase or a decrease in an asset or liability or capital will result in either a debit or a credit to the asset, liability or capital accounts.

Indicate with a tick whether a debit or credit will result from the transactions in the column on the left.

Transaction	Debit	Credit
(a) Capital account increases		
(b) Liability account increases		
(c) Asset account decreases		
(d) Liability account decreases		
(e) Asset account increases		

3.8 The table below sets out account balances from the books of a business. The opening capital is £20,000 which has been paid into the business bank account.

The columns (a) to (f) show the account balances resulting from a series of financial transactions that have taken place over time.

You are to compare each set of adjacent columns, ie (a) with (b), (b) with (c), and so on and state, with figures, what financial transactions have taken place in each case. The first has been completed for you.

Ignore VAT.

	(a)	(b)	(c)	(d)	(e)	(f)
	£	£	£	£	£	£
Assets						
Vehicles	–	10,000	10,000	10,000	18,000	18,000
Inventory	–	–	6,000	9,000	9,000	9,000
Bank	20,000	10,000	4,000	4,000	1,000	11,000
Liabilities						
Loan	–	–	–	–	5,000	5,000
Payables	–	–	–	3,000	3,000	3,000
Capital	20,000	20,000	20,000	20,000	20,000	30,000

Answer (a) - (b): Vehicles have been bought for £10,000, paid from the bank

3.9 Enter the transactions listed below in the double-entry accounts. All the transactions pass through the Bank account so you will have to write the entries in the Bank account and work out what the other account entry will be. No credit sales or purchases are involved.

You can draw up your own accounts, photocopy the accounts on page 69 of the Tutorial, or download blank accounts from the Osborne Books website (www.osbornebooks.co.uk).

Date 20-4	Transaction
4 March	Paid in capital of £5,000
5 March	Received bank loan of £15,000
7 March	Sales of £670
11 March	Purchases of £375
15 March	Paid rent of £400
16 March	Purchases of £1,380
18 March	Sales of £430
22 March	Paid telephone bill £180
26 March	Sales of £1,320
29 March	Paid insurance of £1,200

3.10   The date is 31 August 20-4. You work as a bookkeeper for Beechwood Tools, a business that sells tools and equipment to the construction trade. You have been asked to balance the four accounts shown below.

(a)

Dr			Egret Building (Sales Ledger)		Cr
20-4	**Details**	**£**	**20-4**	**Details**	**£**
24 Aug	Sales	900.00	25 Aug	Sales returns	160.00
27 Aug	Sales	140.00			
28 Aug	Sales	360.00			

(b)

Dr			Curtis & Curtis (Purchases Ledger)		Cr
20-4	**Details**	**£**	**20-4**	**Details**	**£**
			24 Aug	Purchases	496.00
			26 Aug	Purchases	157.50
			31 Aug	Purchases	360.00

(c)

Dr	R & T Engineering (Purchases Ledger)				Cr	
20-4	**Details**	**£**	**20-4**	**Details**		**£**
24 Aug	Purchases returns	160.00	25 Aug	Purchases		240.00
			28 Aug	Purchases		720.00
			31 Aug	Purchases		340.00

(d)

Dr	Motor expenses (General Ledger)				Cr	
20-4	**Details**	**£**	**20-4**	**Details**		**£**
5 Aug	Bank	150.40				
7 Aug	Bank	382.00				
9 Aug	Bank	69.30				
16 Aug	Bank	126.90				

4   Accounting for sales, returns and discounts

4.1   Which **one** of the following is a financial document?

(a) Sales day book	
(b) Credit note	
(c) Sales ledger account of P Lane	
(d) Sales account	

4.2   Which **one** of the following is in the right order?

(a) Sales returns account; sales ledger control account; customer's account; credit note issued; sales returns day book	
(b) Sales returns day book; sales ledger control account; customer's account; sales returns account; credit note issued	
(c) Sales returns day book; credit note issued; customer's account; sales returns account; sales ledger control account	
(d) Credit note issued; sales returns day book; sales returns account; sales ledger control account; customer's account	

4.3   Which **one** of the following is entered in the sales day book?

(a) Credit note	
(b) Purchase order	
(c) Statement of account sent to B Roberts, a trade receivable	
(d) Invoice	

For Activities 4.4 and 4.5:

* work in pounds and pence, where appropriate

* the rate of Value Added Tax is to be calculated at 20% (when calculating VAT amounts, you should ignore fractions of a penny, ie round down to a whole penny)

* use a coding system incorporating the following:

sales day book — SDB65	*general ledger account numbers*
sales returns day book — SRDB22	*sales ledger control account* – GL1200
	sales account – GL4100
sales ledger account numbers	*sales returns account* – GL4110
Dines Stores — SL086	*Value Added Tax account* – GL2200
Meadow Golf Club — SL135	
Raven Retailers Ltd — SL170	
Teme Sports Ltd — SL178	
Wyvern Stores — SL195	

4.4 Pensax Products Limited manufactures and sells sports goods. During November 20-4 the following credit transactions took place:

20-4

3 Nov   Sold goods to Dines Stores £265 + VAT, invoice no 3592 issued

5 Nov   Sold goods to Raven Retailers Limited £335 + VAT, invoice no 3593 issued

6 Nov   Sold goods to Meadow Golf Club £175 + VAT, invoice no 3594 issued

10 Nov   Sold goods to Wyvern Stores £455 + VAT, invoice no 3595 issued

11 Nov   Sold goods to Dines Stores £290 + VAT, invoice no 3596 issued

13 Nov   Sold goods to Teme Sports Limited £315 + VAT, invoice no 3597 issued

17 Nov   Sold goods to Raven Retailers Limited £1,120 + VAT, invoice no 3598 issued

19 Nov   Sold goods to Teme Sports Limited £825 + VAT, invoice no 3599 issued

21 Nov   Sold goods to Dines Stores £354 + VAT, invoice no 3600 issued

24 Nov   Sold goods to Meadow Golf Club £248 + VAT, invoice no 3601 issued

27 Nov   Sold goods to Wyvern Stores £523 + VAT, invoice no 3602 issued

You are to:

(a) Enter the above transactions in Pensax Products' sales day book for November 20-4, using the format shown on the next page.

(b) Record the accounting entries in Pensax Products' general ledger and sales ledger. (You will need to retain the ledger accounts for use with Activity 4.5.).

Sales Day Book						SDB65
Date	Details	Invoice number	Account code	Total £	VAT £	Net £

4.5   The following details are the sales returns of Pensax Products Limited for November 20-4. They are to be:

(a)   Entered in the sales returns day book for November 20-4, using the format shown on the next page.

(b)   Recorded in the general ledger and sales ledger (use the ledgers already prepared in the answer to Activity 4.4).

20-4

10 Nov   Dines Stores returns goods £55 + VAT, credit note no 831 issued

14 Nov   Wyvern Stores returns goods £60 + VAT, credit note no 832 issued

19 Nov   Meadow Golf Club returns goods £46 + VAT, credit note no 833 issued

24 Nov   Teme Sports Limited returns goods £127 + VAT, credit note no 834 issued

28 Nov   Dines Stores returns goods £87 + VAT, credit note no 835 issued

		Sales Returns Day Book				SRDB22
Date	Details	Credit note number	Account code	Total £	VAT £	Net £

4.6 Sales invoices have been prepared and partially entered in the sales day book, as shown below.

(a) Complete the entries in the sales day book by inserting the appropriate figures for each invoice.

(b) Total the last five columns of the sales day book.

Sales day book

Date 20-4	Details	Invoice number	Total £	VAT £	Net £	Sales type 1 £	Sales type 2 £
30 June	Olander Ltd	1895		320		1,600	
30 June	Boltz & Co	1896	5,040				4,200
30 June	Ravells	1897	576		480	480	
	Totals						

4.7 You are employed by Beacon Limited as an Accounts Assistant. The business has a manual accounting system. Double-entry takes place in the general ledger; individual accounts of trade receivables are kept as subsidiary accounts in the sales ledger. The VAT rate is 20%.

Notes:

- show your answer with a tick, words or figures, as appropriate
- coding is not required

(a) The following credit transactions all took place on 30 June 20-7 and have been entered into the sales day book as shown below. No entries have yet been made in the ledgers.

Sales day book

Date 20-7	Details	Invoice number	Total £	VAT £	Net £
30 June	Upton Ltd	407	2,016	336	1,680
30 June	Bromyards	408	3,408	568	2,840
30 June	Kempsey & Co	409	4,272	712	3,560
30 June	Fernhill plc	410	2,448	408	2,040
	Totals		12,144	2,024	10,120

What will be the entries in the sales ledger?

Select your account names from the following list: Bromyards, Discounts allowed, Discounts received, Fernhill plc, Kempsey & Co, Purchases, Purchases ledger control, Purchases returns, Sales, Sales ledger control, Sales returns, Upton Ltd, Value Added Tax.

Sales ledger

Account name	Amount £	Debit	Credit

What will be the entries in the general ledger?

Select your account names from the following list: Discounts allowed, Discounts received, Purchases, Purchases ledger control, Purchases returns, Sales, Sales ledger control, Sales returns, Value Added Tax.

General ledger

Account name	Amount £	Debit	Credit

(b) The following credit transactions all took place on 30 June 20-7 and have been entered into the sales returns day book as shown below. No entries have yet been made in the ledgers.

Sales returns day book

Date 20-7	Details	Credit note number	Total £	VAT £	Net £
30 June	Drake & Co	CN 84	336	56	280
30 June	Hanbury Trading	CN 85	1,008	168	840
	Totals		1,344	224	1,120

What will be the entries in the sales ledger?

Select your account names from the following list: Discounts allowed, Discounts received, Drake & Co, Hanbury Trading, Purchases, Purchases ledger control, Purchases returns, Sales, Sales ledger control, Sales returns, Value Added Tax.

Sales ledger

Account name	Amount £	Debit	Credit

What will be the entries in the general ledger?

Select your account names from the following list: Discounts allowed, Discounts received, Purchases, Purchases ledger control, Purchases returns, Sales, Sales ledger control, Sales returns, Value Added Tax.

General ledger

Account name	Amount £	Debit	Credit

(c)   The following discounts allowed transactions all took place on 30 June 20-7 and have been entered into the discounts allowed day book as shown below. No entries have yet been made in the ledgers.

Discounts allowed day book

Date 20-7	Details	Credit note number	Total £	VAT £	Net £
30 June	Powick & Co	DA 58	30	5	25
30 June	Heath Trading	DA 59	42	7	35
	Totals		72	12	60

What will be the entries in the sales ledger?

Select your account names from the following list: Discounts allowed, Discounts received, Heath Trading, Powick & Co, Purchases, Purchases ledger control, Purchases returns, Sales, Sales ledger control, Sales returns, Value Added Tax.

Sales ledger

Account name	Amount £	Debit	Credit

What will be the entries in the general ledger?

Select your account names from the following list: Discounts allowed, Discounts received, Purchases, Purchases ledger control, Purchases returns, Sales, Sales ledger control, Sales returns, Value Added Tax.

General ledger

Account name	Amount £	Debit	Credit

4.8   These are the totals of the discounts allowed day book at the end of the month.

Discounts allowed day book

Details	Total £	VAT £	Net £
Totals	144	24	120

(a)   What will be the entries in the general ledger?

Select your account names from the following list: Discounts allowed, Discounts received, Purchases, Purchases ledger control, Purchases returns, Sales, Sales ledger control, Sales returns, VAT.

General ledger

Account name	Amount £	Debit	Credit

One of the entries in the discounts allowed day book is for a credit note sent to Khan Ltd for £55 plus VAT.

(b)   What will be the entry in the sales ledger?

Select your account name from the following list: Discounts allowed, Discounts received, Khan Ltd, Purchases, Purchases ledger control, Purchases returns, Sales, Sales ledger control, Sales returns, VAT.

Sales ledger

Account name	Amount £	Debit	Credit

4.9 You are the bookkeeper at Rankin Ltd.

Four sales invoices have been issued and have been partially entered in the analysed sales day book, shown below.

Complete the entries in the sales day book by inserting the appropriate details from each invoice, and then total the day book.

INVOICE NO 2132	30 June 20-4
From: Rankin Ltd	
18 Blenheim Road	
Linton	
LT4 5JE	
VAT Registration No 264 1432 55	

To:	Hawke Ltd	£
	30 items of product T12 @ £10 each	300.00
	VAT @ 20%	60.00
	Total	360.00

INVOICE NO 2133	30 June 20-4
From: Rankin Ltd	
18 Blenheim Road	
Linton	
LT4 5JE	
VAT Registration No 264 1432 55	

To:	T Martin	£
	25 items of product S12 @ £15 each	375.00
	VAT @ 20%	75.00
	Total	450.00

```
INVOICE NO 2134                           30 June 20-4

From:  Rankin Ltd

       18 Blenheim Road

       Linton

       LT4 5JE

       VAT Registration No 264 1432 55
```

To:	S Garner	£
	35 items of product S12 @ £15 each	525.00
	VAT @ 20%	105.00
	Total	630.00

```
INVOICE NO 2135                           30 June 20-4

From:  Rankin Ltd

       18 Blenheim Road

       Linton

       LT4 5JE

       VAT Registration No 264 1432 55
```

To:	JEC Ltd	£
	15 items of product T12 @ £10 each	150.00
	VAT @ 20%	30.00
	Total	180.00

Sales day book

Date 20-4	Details	Invoice number	Total £	VAT £	Net £	Product S12 £	Product T12 £
30 June	Hawke Ltd						
30 June	T Martin						
30 June	S Garner						
30 June	JEC Ltd						
	Totals						

5 Process payments from customers

5.1 A business receiving a remittance advice from a customer will need to check it against the sales documents. Which of the following checks is required?

Choose the correct option.

(a) Sales documention reference numbers	
(b) The number of the cheque	
(c) Bank account number	
(d) Date of the remittance advice	

5.2 A business receiving a cheque from a customer in payment of an invoice will need to check it to make sure that it is in order. Which of the following list of checks is correct?

Choose the appropriate option.

(a) Date, signature, bank account number	
(b) Date, signature, bank sort code	
(c) Same amount in words and figures, in date, signature of customer	
(d) Same amount in words and figures, in date, invoice number	

5.3 The account shown below is in the sales ledger of Johnston & Co. Also shown below is a BACS remittance advice received from R Romero at the end of August.

R Romero					
Date 20-4	Details	Amount £	Date 20-4	Details	Amount £
1 Aug	Balance b/f	2,790	2 Aug	Bank	2,790
10 Aug	Sales invoice 392	690	26 June	Sales returns credit note 295	90
25 Aug	Sales Invoice 417	1,100			

R Romero

BACS REMITTANCE ADVICE

To: Johnston & Co   Date: 28 August 20-4

The following payment will reach your bank account within 3 working days.

Invoice number	Credit note number	Amount £
392		590
417		1,100
Total amount paid		1,690

You are required to check the remittance advice against the sales ledger account.

State two discrepancies you can identify:

(a)

(b)

6 Process documents from suppliers

6.1 When a credit note is received by the buyer in respect of faulty goods returned by the buyer, it should be checked against the details on the:

(a) Invoice	
(b) Delivery note	
(c) Remittance advice	

Tick the appropriate box.

6.2 A business will use supplier codes to refer to accounts in:

(a) The general ledger	
(b) The sales ledger	
(c) The purchases ledger	

Tick the appropriate box.

6.3 A business will use general ledger codes to refer to accounts for:

(a) Purchases	
(b) Suppliers	
(c) Customers	

Tick the appropriate box.

6.4   A supply of office chairs has been delivered to Praxis Stationery. Praxis Stationery completes a Goods Received Note as shown below.

Examine the note and answer the questions below by selecting the correct words from the following list:

Praxis Stationery	**2 chairs missing**	**2 chairs damaged**	**purchases day book**
credit note	**Helicon Furniture**	**debit note**	**sales day book**
sales ledger	**returns note**	**refund note**	**purchase ledeger**

GOODS RECEIVED NOTE
PRAXIS STATIONERY

GRN no.   302

supplier   Helicon Furniture

date   4 December 20-4

order ref.	quantity	description
8246	10	Office chairs (Code Typ72652)

received by *D Nutt* .... checked by *N Mason* ....

condition of goods   condition - *good (8 chairs)*

damages - *2 chairs damaged*

shortages *none*

(a)   Who has supplied the chairs?

(b)   What is the problem with the consignment?

(c)   What document would be issued by the supplier to adjust the account of Praxis Stationery?

(d)   Where in the supplier's accounting records would the account of Praxis Stationery be maintained?

6.5 A supply of office chairs has been delivered to Praxis Stationery by Firth Furniture. The purchase order sent from Praxis Stationery, and the invoice from Firth Furniture, are shown below.

PURCHASE ORDER
PRAXIS STATIONERY

No 1066

Date 10 08 20-3

45 Jarvis Street, Mereford MR1 2GH

To: Firth Furniture

Please supply 12 Executive office chairs (product code EXCH45)

Purchase price: £150 each, plus VAT @ 20%

Discount: less 20% trade discount, as agreed

INVOICE
FIRTH FURNITURE
17 Chippendale Street
Lesspool LP1 5HG
VAT Reg 171 7326 11

To:
Praxis Stationery
45 Jarvis Street, Mereford MR1 2GH

Date 11 08 20-3
No. 6518
Account PS6232

Quantity	Product code	Price (£)	Total (£)	Net (£)	VAT (£)	Total (£)
12	EXCH45	150.00	1,800.00	1,620.00	324.00	1,944.00

Check the invoice against the purchase order and answer the following questions:

Has the correct purchase price of the chairs been charged? Yes or No?	
Has the correct discount been applied? Yes or No?	
What would be the VAT amount charged if the invoice was correct?	£
What would be the total amount charged if the invoice was correct?	£

6.6 A supply of office desks has been delivered to Praxis Stationery by Firth Furniture. The purchase order sent from Praxis Stationery, and the delivery note from Firth Furniture, are shown below.

PURCHASE ORDER
PRAXIS STATIONERY

No 1261
Date 05 09 20-3

45 Jarvis Street, Mereford MR1 2GH

To: Firth Furniture

Please supply 4 oak finish office tables (product code OTT28)

Purchase price: £80 each, plus VAT @ 20%.

Discount: less 20% trade discount, as agreed.

DELIVERY NOTE
FIRTH FURNITURE
17 Chippendale Street
Lesspool LP1 5HG
VAT Reg 171 7326 11

To:
Praxis Stationery
45 Jarvis Street, Mereford MR1 2GH

Date 10 09 20-3
No. 6610
Account PS6232

Quantity	Product code	Description
5	OTT28	Office tables, teak finish (product code OTT28) @ £80 each, less trade discount @ 20%, plus VAT @ 20%.

Check the delivery note against the purchase order and answer the following questions:

Has the correct number of tables been supplied? Yes or No?	
Has the correct type of table been supplied? Yes or No?	
What will be the total of the invoice on the basis of the details on the delivery note?	£
If a credit note were issued, what would be the total, including VAT?	£

7 Accounting for purchases, returns and discounts

7.1 Which **one** of the following is a financial document?

(a) Purchases invoice	
(b) Statement of account sent by T Lewis, a trade payable	
(c) Purchases day book	
(d) Purchases ledger control account	

7.2 Which **one** of the following is in the right order?

(a) Purchases day book; purchases ledger control account; invoice received; purchases account; supplier's account	
(b) Purchases account; supplier's account; purchases ledger control account; purchases day book; invoice received	
(c) Invoice received; purchases day book; purchases account; purchases ledger control account; supplier's account	
(d) Invoice received; purchases account; purchases ledger control account; supplier's account; purchases day book	

7.3 Which **one** of the following shows the correct general ledger entries to record the purchase of goods for resale on credit?

(a) Debit purchases ledger control; debit VAT; credit purchases	
(b) Debit purchases ledger control; credit purchases; credit VAT	
(c) Debit purchases; debit VAT; credit purchases ledger control	
(d) Debit purchases; credit purchases ledger control; credit VAT	

For Activities 7.4 and 7.5:

• work in pounds and pence, where appropriate

• the rate of Value Added Tax is to be calculated at 20% (when calculating VAT amounts, you should ignore fractions of a penny, ie round down to a whole penny)

• use a coding system incorporating the following:

purchases day book	– PDB55		
purchases returns day book	– PRDB14	general ledger account numbers	
		purchases ledger control account	– GL2350
purchases ledger account numbers		purchases account	– GL5100
S Burston	– PL530	purchases returns account	– GL5110
Iley Supplies Ltd	– PL605	Value Added Tax account	– GL2200
Malvern Manufacturing	– PL625		
SG Enterprises	– PL720		

7.4   Wyvern Products Limited manufactures and sells garden furniture. During May 20-2 the following credit transactions took place:

20-2

3 May   Purchased goods from Malvern Manufacturing £170 + VAT, invoice no 7321

9 May   Purchased goods from S Burston £265 + VAT, invoice no SB745

12 May   Purchased goods from Iley Supplies Ltd £450 + VAT, invoice no 4721

18 May   Purchased goods from SG Enterprises £825 + VAT, invoice no 3947

23 May   Purchased goods from S Burston £427 + VAT, invoice no SB773

30 May   Purchased goods from Malvern Manufacturing £364 + VAT, invoice no 7408

You are to:

(a)   Enter the above transactions in Wyvern Products Limited's purchases day book for May 20-2, using the format shown on the next page.

(b)   Record the accounting entries in Wyvern Products Limited's general ledger and purchases ledger. (You will need to retain the ledger accounts for use with Activity 7.5).

Purchases Day Book						PDB55
Date	Details	Invoice number	Account code	Total £	VAT £	Net £

7.5 The following are the purchases returns of Wyvern Products Limited for May 20-2. They are to be:

(a) Entered in the purchases returns day book for May 20-2, using the format shown on the next page.

(b) Recorded in the general ledger and purchases ledger (use the ledgers already prepared in the answer to Activity 7.4).

20-2

11 May   Returned goods to Malvern Manufacturing £70 + VAT, credit note no CN345 received

17 May   Returned goods to Iley Supplies Ltd £85 + VAT, credit note no CN241 received

24 May   Returned goods to SG Enterprises £25 + VAT, credit note no 85 received

31 May   Returned goods to S Burston £55 + VAT, credit note no SB95 received

Purchases Returns Day Book						PRDB14
Date	Details	Invoice number	Account code	Total £	VAT £	Net £

7.6 Purchases invoices have been prepared and partially entered in the purchases day book, as shown below.

(a) Complete the entries in the purchases day book by inserting the appropriate figures for each invoice.

(b) Total the last five columns of the purchases day book.

Purchases day book

Date 20-4	Details	Invoice number	Total £	VAT £	Net £	Purchases type 1 £	Purchases type 2 £
30 June	King & Co	K641	2,016		1,680		1,680
30 June	Rossingtons	2129		512		2,560	
30 June	Moniz Ltd	M/149	2,208				1,840
	Totals						

7.7 You are employed by Churchtown Limited as an Accounts Assistant. The business has a manual accounting system. Double-entry takes place in the general ledger; individual accounts of trade payables are kept as subsidiary accounts in the purchases ledger. The VAT rate is 20%.

Notes:

- show your answer with a tick, words or figures, as appropriate
- coding is not required

(a) The following credit transactions all took place on 30 June 20-8 and have been entered into the purchases day book as shown below. No entries have yet been made in the ledgers.

Purchases day book

Date 20-8	Details	Invoice number	Total £	VAT £	Net £
30 June	H & L Ltd	5986	6,528	1,088	5,440
30 June	Sperrin & Co	P864	2,208	368	1,840
30 June	Hickmores	H591	4,608	768	3,840
30 June	Marklew plc	6417	1,104	184	920
	Totals		14,448	2,408	12,040

What will be the entries in the purchases ledger?

Select your account names from the following list: Discounts allowed, Discounts received, H & L Ltd, Hickmores, Marklew plc, Purchases, Purchases ledger control, Purchases returns, Sales, Sales ledger control, Sales returns, Sperrin & Co, Value Added Tax.

Purchases ledger

Account name	Amount £	Debit	Credit

What will be the entries in the general ledger?

Select your account names from the following list: Discounts allowed, Discounts received, Purchases, Purchases ledger control, Purchases returns, Sales, Sales ledger control, Sales returns, Value Added Tax.

General ledger

Account name	Amount £	Debit	Credit

(b) The following credit transactions all took place on 30 June 20-8 and have been entered into the purchases returns day book as shown below. No entries have yet been made in the ledgers.

Purchases returns day book

Date 20-8	Details	Credit note number	Total £	VAT £	Net £
30 June	Marcer Transport	564	624	104	520
30 June	Schuller Ltd	CN28	432	72	360
	Totals		1,056	176	880

What will be the entries in the purchases ledger?

Select your account names from the following list: Discounts allowed, Discounts received, Marcer Transport, Purchases, Purchases ledger control, Purchases returns, Sales, Sales ledger control, Sales returns, Schuller Ltd, Value Added Tax.

Purchases ledger

Account name	Amount £	Debit	Credit

What will be the entries in the general ledger?

Select your account names from the following list: Discounts allowed, Discounts received, Purchases, Purchases ledger control, Purchases returns, Sales, Sales ledger control, Sales returns, Value Added Tax.

General ledger

Account name	Amount £	Debit	Credit

(c)   The following discounts received transactions all took place on 30 June 20-8 and have been entered into the discounts received day book as shown below. No entries have yet been made in the ledgers.

Discounts received day book

Date 20-8	Details	Credit note number	Total £	VAT £	Net £
30 June	DDE & Co	CN141	18	3	15
30 June	Transpo Ltd	CN28	24	4	20
	Totals		42	7	35

What will be the entries in the purchases ledger?

Select your account names from the following list: DDE & Co, Discounts allowed, Discounts received, Purchases, Purchases ledger control, Purchases returns, Sales, Sales ledger control, Sales returns, Transpo Ltd, Value Added Tax.

Purchases ledger

Account name	Amount £	Debit	Credit

What will be the entries in the general ledger?

Select your account names from the following list: Discounts allowed, Discounts received, Purchases, Purchases ledger control, Purchases returns, Sales, Sales ledger control, Sales returns, Value Added Tax.

General ledger

Account name	Amount £	Debit	Credit

7.8 These are the totals of the discounts received day book at the end of the month.

Discounts received day book

Details	Total £	VAT £	Net £
Totals	234	39	195

(a) What will be the entries in the general ledger?

Select your account names from the following list: Discounts allowed, Discounts received, Purchases, Purchases ledger control, Purchases returns, Sales, Sales ledger control, Sales returns, VAT.

General ledger

Account name	Amount £	Debit	Credit

One of the entries in the discounts received day book is for a credit note received from Hussain plc for £85 plus VAT.

(b) What will be the entry in the purchases ledger?

Select your account name from the following list: Discounts allowed, Discounts received, Hussain plc, Purchases, Purchases ledger control, Purchases returns, Sales, Sales ledger control, Sales returns, VAT.

Purchases ledger

Account name	Amount £	Debit	Credit

7.9   You are the bookkeeper at Rankin Ltd.

Four purchases invoices have been received and have been partially entered in the analysed purchases day book, shown below.

Complete the entries in the purchases day book by inserting the appropriate details from each invoice, and then total the day book.

INVOICE NO 4681	30 June 20-4
From: Lyster Ltd	
44 Mill Street	
Linton	
LT3 6AJ	
VAT Registration No 451 3268 01	

To:	Rankin Ltd	£
	100 items of product S12 @ £10 each	1,000.00
	VAT @ 20%	200.00
	Total	1,200.00

INVOICE NO 6234	30 June 20-4
From: T England	
14 Nelson Street	
Westerham	
WH6 9JK	
VAT Registration No 323 8614 25	

To:	Rankin Ltd	£
	60 items of product T12 @ £6 each	360.00
	VAT @ 20%	72.00
	Total	432.00

INVOICE NO 1634   30 June 20-4

From: **Mere Ltd**

      22 Moreton Road

      Ruddington

      RT5 2BN

      VAT Registration No 495 0232 55

To:	Rankin Ltd	£
	150 items of product T12 @ £6 each	900.00
	VAT @ 20%	180.00
	Total	1,080.00

INVOICE NO 8561   30 June 20-4

From: **J Mehta**

      84 The High Road

      Linton

      LT1 2DS

      VAT Registration No 264 9781 65

To:	Rankin Ltd	£
	40 items of product S12 @ £10 each	400.00
	VAT @ 20%	80.00
	Total	480.00

Purchases day book

Date 20-4	Details	Invoice number	Total £	VAT £	Net £	Product S12 £	Product T12 £
30 June	Lyster Ltd						
30 June	T England						
30 June	Mere Ltd						
30 June	J Mehta						
	Totals						

8 Prepare payments to suppliers

8.1   If a supplier duplicates an invoice for goods ordered, the likely effect will be:

(a) An increase in the total amount owing shown on the statement of account	
(b) A decrease in the total amount owing shown on the statement of account	
(c) No effect at all	

Tick the appropriate box.

8.2   A remittance advice is likely to show details of the following financial documents issued:

(a) Purchase invoices, purchase credit notes, goods received notes	
(b) Purchase invoices, purchase credit notes, cheques issued	
(c) Purchase invoices, purchase credit notes, total amount owing	

Tick the appropriate box.

8.3   The purchase ledger account of a supplier shows a purchase invoice which is not shown on the supplier's statement of account. This:

(a) Can be adjusted by asking the supplier to issue a credit note	
(b) Will reduce the total amount shown as owing on the statement of account	
(c) Will increase the total amount shown as owing on the statement of account	

Tick the appropriate box.

8.4 Shown below is a statement of account received from Masters Supplies, a credit supplier, and the supplier's account as shown in the purchases ledger of Broadfield Traders.

Masters Supplies

21 HighStreet, East Mereford, MR7 9HJ

To: Broadfield Traders

Unit 18 Elgar Estate

Mereford, MR2 5FG   **STATEMENT OF ACCOUNT**

Date 20-4	Invoice Number	Details	Invoice Amount £	Cheque Amount £	Balance £
1 May	699	Goods	2,000		2,000
5 May	712	Goods	1,100		3,100
9 May	731	Goods	750		3,850
28 May	790	Goods	1,360		5,210
1 June	-	Cheque		3,850	1,360

	Masters Supplies					
Date 20-4	Details	Amount £	Date 20-4	Details		Amount £
1 June	Bank	3,850	1 May	Purchases		2,000
28 June	Bank	1,000	8 May	Purchases		1,100
			10 May	Purchases		750

(a) Which item is missing from the statement of account from Masters Supplies? Select your answer from the following list:

Invoice 699, Invoice 712, Invoice 731, Invoice 790, Cheque for £3,850, Cheque for £1,000

(b) Which item is missing from the supplier account in Broadfield Traders' purchases ledger? Select your answer from the following list:

Invoice 699, Invoice 712, Invoice 731, Invoice 790, Cheque for £3,850, Cheque for £1,000

(c) Assuming any differences between the statement of account from Masters Supplies and the supplier account in Broadfield Traders' purchases ledger are simply due to omission errors, what is the amount owing to Masters Supplies?

£

8.5   Mereford Traders sends BACS remittance advice notes to suppliers on the last day of the month following the month of invoice. Mereford Traders banks with National Bank plc and A Strauss & Co banks with Mercia Bank plc. Below is an uncompleted BACS remittance advice and an extract from Mereford Trader's purchases ledger.

<table>
<tr><td colspan="3" align="center">**Mereford Traders**
45 College Street
Mereford, MR3 4GT

BACS REMITTANCE ADVICE</td></tr>
<tr><td colspan="2">To:</td><td>Date:</td></tr>
<tr><td colspan="3">The following payment will reach your bank account within 3 working days.</td></tr>
<tr><td>**Invoice number**</td><td>**Credit note number**</td><td>**Amount**
£</td></tr>
<tr><td></td><td></td><td></td></tr>
<tr><td></td><td>Total amount paid</td><td></td></tr>
</table>

<table>
<tr><td colspan="6" align="center">**A Strauss & Co**</td></tr>
<tr><td>**Date**
20-4</td><td>**Details**</td><td>**Amount**
£</td><td>**Date**
20-4</td><td>**Details**</td><td>**Amount**
£</td></tr>
<tr><td>3 Feb</td><td>Purchases returns credit note CN101</td><td>400</td><td>15 Feb</td><td>Purchases Invoice 2250</td><td>1,750</td></tr>
<tr><td>20 Mar</td><td>Purchases returns credit note CN105</td><td>300</td><td>12 Mar</td><td>Purchases Invoice 2461</td><td>2,340</td></tr>
<tr><td>30 Mar</td><td>Bank</td><td>1,350</td><td>29 Mar</td><td>Purchases Invoice 2479</td><td>1,600</td></tr>
<tr><td></td><td></td><td></td><td>10 Apr</td><td>Purchases Invoice 2499</td><td>2,107</td></tr>
</table>

(a)   The BACS remittance advice will be sent:

<table>
<tr><td>(a)   With a cheque to Mereford Traders</td><td></td></tr>
<tr><td>(b)   Without a cheque to A Strauss & Co</td><td></td></tr>
<tr><td>(c)   To Mercia Bank plc with a cheque</td><td></td></tr>
<tr><td>(d)   To Mercia Bank plc without a cheque</td><td></td></tr>
</table>

Select the correct option.

(b)   What will be the date shown on the BACS remittance advice?

(a) 28 February	
(b) 31 March	
(c) 30 April	
(d) 31 May	

Select the correct option.

(c)   What will be the items shown on the BACS remittance advice?

(a) Invoice 2250, Invoice 2461, invoice 2479, invoice 2687	
(b) Invoice 2461, invoice 2479, credit note CN105	
(c) Invoice 2250, Invoice 2461, invoice 2479, credit note CN101	
(d) Invoice 2250, Invoice 2461, credit note CN101, credit note CN105	

Select the correct option.

(d)   The amount of the remittance advice will be:

(a) £3,390	
(b) £4,990	
(c) £3,640	
(d) £5,390	

Select the correct option.

9 Cash book

9.1 Which **one** of the following transactions will be recorded on the receipts side of cash book?

(a) Bank charges for £55	
(b) Payment of VAT to HM Revenue & Customs for £1,820	
(c) BACS transfer from a trade receivable for £1,950	
(d) Drawings made by the owner of the business for £750	

9.2 The following transactions all took place on 30 June and have been entered in the debit side of the cash book of Jane Martin, as shown below. No entries have yet been made in the ledgers.

Note that Jane Martin's business is not registered for Value Added Tax.

Cash book – debit side

Date 20-4	Details	Cash £	Bank £
30 June	Balance b/f		2,076
30 June	Delta & Co		325
30 June	Boscawen Ltd		1,540

(a) What will be the entries in the sales ledger?

Select your account names from the following list: Balance b/f, Bank, Boscawen Ltd, Delta & Co, Purchases ledger control, Sales ledger control.

Sales ledger

Account name	Amount £	Debit	Credit

(b) What will be the entries in the general ledger?

Select your account names from the following list: Balance b/f, Bank, Boscawen Ltd, Delta & Co, Purchases ledger control, Sales ledger control.

General ledger

Account name	Amount £	Debit	Credit

The following transactions all took place on 30 June and have been entered in the credit side of the cash book of Jane Martin, as shown below. No entries have yet been made in the ledgers.

Cash book – credit side

Date 20-4	Details	Cash £	Bank £
30 June	Wages	1,265	
30 June	Office equipment		1,968

(c) What will be the entries in the general ledger?

Select your account name from the following list: Bank, Office equipment, Purchases ledger control, Sales ledger control, Wages.

General ledger

Account name	Amount £	Debit	Credit

9.3 The following transactions all took place on 30 June 20-4 and have been entered into the cash book of Rafe Sadler, as shown below. No entries have yet been made in the ledgers.

Note that Rafe Sadler's business is not registered for Value Added Tax.

Dr	Cash Book						CB73 Cr	
Date	Details	Cash	Bank	Date	Details	Cash	Bank
20-4		£	£	20-4		£	£
30 Jun	Balances b/f	250	3,840	30 Jun	Wages		1,175
30 Jun	Smithsons Ltd			30 Jun	Rent		1,200
	(trade receivable)		2,325	30 Jun	Stationery	120	
30 Jun	Egerton & Co			30 Jun	Balances c/d	130	4,215
	(trade receivable)		425				
		250	6,590			250	6,590
1 Jul	Balances b/d	130	4,215				

(a) What will be the entries in the sales ledger?

Select your account names from the following list: Balance b/f, Bank, Egerton & Co, Purchases ledger control, Sales Ledger control, Smithsons Ltd.

Sales ledger

Account name	Amount £	Debit	Credit

(b) What will be the entries in the general ledger?

Select your account names from the following list: Balance b/f, Bank, Purchases ledger control, Rent, Sales ledger control, Stationery, Smithsons Ltd, Wages.

General ledger

Account name	Amount £	Debit	Credit

9.4 The following cash book shows a number of transactions of Wentworths which all took place on 30 September 20-1:

Dr					**Cash Book**				**CB68 Cr**	
Date	Details	Account code	Cash	Bank	Date	Details	Account code	Cash	Bank	
20-1			£	£	20-1			£	£	
30 Sep	Balances b/f		644	3,045	30 Sep	Nelson Stores (trade payable)			1,940	
30 Sep	Cash sales		88		30 Sep	Cash purchases			192	
30 Sep	Albany Ltd (trade receivable)			1,580	30 Sep	General expenses		128		
30 Sep	Balance c/d			201	30 Sep	Wages			1,254	
					30 Sep	Office equipment			1,440	
					30 Sep	Balance c/d		604		
			732	4,826				732	4,826	
1 Oct	Balance b/d		604		1 Oct	Balance b/d			201	

(a) The bank balance brought forward of £3,045 on 30 September shows that, according to the cash book, the business has money in the bank. True or false?

(b) The bank balance brought down of £201 on 1 October shows that, according to the cash book, the business has money in the bank. True or false?

(c) You are to transfer the data from the cash book into the general ledger of Wentworths. Note that a bank account is not required.

(d) Show the entries in the sales ledger and purchases ledger of Wentworths.

Note: Wentworth's business is not registered for Value Added Tax.

9.5 The balances in Sally Henshaw's cash book at 3 August 20-7 were as follows:

	£
Cash in hand	286
Bank overdraft	3,472

The following transactions took place:

3 Aug	Paid rent by cheque £760
4 Aug	Sales £334, cash received
5 Aug	Received a cheque of £1,475 from Murphy Ltd in full settlement of a debt of £1,490
8 Aug	Paid rates by direct debit £223
8 Aug	Paid JJ Supplies by cheque £490 after deducting £10 prompt payment discount
10 Aug	Drawings, £400 by cheque, made by Sally Henshaw
10 Aug	Paid wages £480 in cash

Required:
· Enter the above transactions in the cash book on the next page.
· Balance the cash and bank columns at 10 August 20-7, and bring the balances down on 11 August 20-7.

Note: Sally Henshaw's business is not registered for Value Added Tax.

Cash Book

Dr					Cr	
Date 20-7	Details	Cash £	Bank £	Date 20-7	Details	Cash £	Bank £

9.6 Emma Maxwell uses a cash book as part of her double-entry bookkeeping system. The following details relate to March 20-3.

March		£
1	Balance of cash	200
	Overdrawn bank balance	1,898
2	Bank payment made to Lindum Supplies in settlement of an invoice for £260	254
6	Cheque from Court Ltd paid into bank	1,236
11	Paid rent by cheque	550
13	BACS transfer received from H Sweeney. Prompt payment discount of £10 has been taken by the customer	1,696
14	Sales, cash received	639
23	Paid wages in cash	655
24	Sales, cash received	786
26	Standing order to Wyvern Council	195
27	Interest charged by bank	45
28	BACS transfer received from Mills and Co Ltd	477

Required:

• Enter the above transactions in the cash book shown on the next page.

• Balance the cash book at the end of the month and bring down the balances at 1 April 20-3.

Note: Emma Maxwell's business is not registered for Value Added Tax.

Cash Book

Dr						Cr	
Date 20-3	Details	Cash £	Bank £	Date 20-3	Details	Cash £	Bank £

9.7 Which **one** of the following transactions will be recorded on the payments side of cash book?

(a) Repayment of VAT by HM Revenue & Customs for £255	
(b) BACS transfer from a trade receivable for £690	
(c) Debit card payment to a trade payable for £940	
(d) Increase in owner's capital by bank transfer for £5,000	

9.8 Show whether the following statements are true or false.

Statement		True	False
(a)	Cash and bank accounts are the general ledger accounts when cash book is used as a book of prime entry only		
(b)	The purchases ledger column total from cash book is credited to purchases ledger control account in general ledger		
(c)	The trade payables column total from an analysed cash book is debited to purchases ledger control account in general ledger		
(d)	The VAT column total on the payments side of cash book is debited to VAT account in general ledger		

9.9 You are an accounts assistant at Denison Limited. One of your duties is to write-up the cash book. There are five payments to be entered in Denison Limited's cash book.

Receipts for cash payments

Received cash with thanks for goods bought.	
From Denison Ltd, a customer without a credit account.	
Net	£40
VAT	£8
Total	£48
Clark & Co	

Received cash with thanks for goods bought.	
From Denison Ltd, a customer without a credit account.	
Net	£160
VAT	£32
Total	£192
T Kinnear	

Bank payments

Gaskin Ltd
(Purchases ledger account PL110)
£1,690

Bristow Stationery
(No credit account with this supplier)
£144 including VAT

Roussouw & Co
(Purchases ledger account PL280)
£1,140

(a) Enter the details from the two receipts for cash payments and the three bank payments into the credit side of the cash book shown below and total each column.

Cash book – credit side

Details	Cash £	Bank £	VAT £	Trade payables £	Cash purchases £	Stationery expenses £
Balance b/f						
Clark & Co						
T Kinnear						
Gaskin Ltd						
Bristow Stationery						
Roussouw & Co						
Totals						

There are two bank receipts from credit customers to be entered in Denison Limited's cash book:

Passmores	£455
S McNulty	£833

(b) Enter the above details into the debit side of the cash book and total each column.

Cash book – debit side

Details	Cash £	Bank £	Trade receivables £
Balance b/f	642	1,022	
Passmores			
S McNulty			
Totals			

(c)   Using your answers to (a) and (b) above, calculate the cash balance.

£ _____

(d)   Using your answers to (a) and (b) above, calculate the bank balance.

£ _____

(e)   Will the bank balance calculated in (d) above be a debit or credit balance?

Debit	
Credit	

9.10   There are four payments to be entered in Rowson Limited's cash book.

Payments to suppliers who do not offer credit accounts:

- cash paid to Mary Wallbank of £192, including VAT, for goods purchased
- a bank payment of £425, no VAT, to Wenton Council for rates

Payments to credit suppliers:

- BACS payments made as authorised on the two invoices shown below.

Sanders plc 2 Albany Road Wenton WT4 8PQ VAT Registration No 208 7641 00	J Panas Market Street South Wenton WT6 4JK VAT Registration No 396 4918 00
Invoice No. 6231 30 June 20-4	Invoice No. I2721 30 June 20-4

To: Rowson Ltd
    14 Blenheim Road
    Wenton, WT2 1XJ
	To: Rowson Ltd
	    14 Blenheim Road
	    Wenton, WT2 1XJ

£ 50 items of AB @ £10.00 each 500.00 VAT @ 20% 100.00 Total 600.00	£ 80 items of AD @ £7.00 each 560.00 VAT @ 20% 112.00 Total 672.00
Authorised for payment in full: T Rowson	Authorised for payment in full: T Rowson
Terms: 30 days net.	*Terms: 30 days net.*

(a)   Enter the details of the four payments into the credit side of the cash book shown below and total each column.

Cash book – credit side

Details	Cash £	Bank £	VAT £	Trade payables £	Cash purchases £	Other expenses £
Balance b/f		2,417				
Totals						

There are three amounts received to be entered in Rowson Limited's cash book.

Cheques received from credit customers:

- LFJ plc £1,685
- Wragg Ltd £2,135

Cash received:

- £200 received from Nikki Shah for rent of office space (No VAT)

(b)   Enter the details of the three receipts into the debit side of the cash book shown below and total each column.

Cash book – debit side

Details	Cash £	Bank £	Trade receivables £	Other income £
Balance b/f	208			
Totals				

(c) Using your answers to (a) and (b) on the previous page, calculate the cash balance.

£ [   ]

(d) Using your answers to (a) and (b) on the previous page, calculate the bank balance. If your calculations show that the bank account is overdrawn your answer should start with a minus sign, for example −123.

£ [   ]

(e) What will be the entry in Wragg Ltd's account in the sales ledger to record the payment received?

Sales ledger

Account name	Amount £	Debit	Credit
Wragg Ltd			

10   Petty cash book

10.1   The imprest system for petty cash means that:

(a) Petty cash payments up to a stated amount can be authorised by the petty cashier	
(b) Petty cash vouchers must have relevant documentation attached	
(c) The petty cash float is restored to the same amount for the beginning of each week or month	
(d) Petty cash vouchers are numbered and the number is recorded in the petty cash book	

10.2   A petty cash account has a balance b/d of £150 at the beginning of a month. During the month, payments are made from petty cash which total £108. Which **one** of the following transactions will restore the balance of petty cash account to £150?

(a) Debit bank £150; credit petty cash £150	
(b) Debit petty cash £108; credit bank £108	
(c) Debit petty cash £42; credit bank £42	
(d) Debit bank £108; credit petty cash £108	

10.3   Show whether the following statements are true or false.

Statement	True	False
(a) Payments are recorded on the debit side of petty cash book		
(b) A petty cash book may combine the roles of a book of prime entry and double-entry bookkeeping		
(c) Petty cash vouchers are authorised for payment by the petty cashier or a manager		
(d) The totals of the petty cash analysis columns are transferred to general ledger where they are debited to the appropriate expense account		

10.4 A firm's petty cash book is operated on the imprest system. The imprest amount is £250. At the end of a particular period, the analysis columns are totalled as follows: VAT £13.42; postage £29.18; travel £45.47; stationery £33.29; cleaning £18.54.

How much cash will be required to restore the imprest amount for the next period?

(a) £250.00	
(b) £126.48	
(c) £139.90	
(d) £110.10	

10.5 A firm's petty cash book is operated on the imprest system. The imprest amount is £125. At the end of a particular period the petty cash remaining comprised:

2 x £10 notes, 5 x £5 notes, 4 x £1 coins, 3 x 50p coins, 6 x 20p coins, 3 x 10p coins, 3 x 5p coins, 8 x 1p coins.

Provided no errors or discrepancies have occurred, what is the amount of payments that will be recorded in the petty cash book for the period?

(a) £72.77	
(b) £52.23	
(c) £72.65	
(d) £125.00	

10.6 The petty cashier of the business where you work tops up the petty cash at the end of the month with £110 withdrawn from the bank.

What will be the entries in the general ledger?

Select your account names from the following list: Bank, Cash, Petty cash book, Purchases, Purchases ledger control, Sales, Sales ledger control, Value Added Tax.

General ledger

Account name	Amount £	Debit	Credit

10.7 Wyvern Property maintains a petty cash book as both a book of prime entry and part of the double-entry accounting system. The following transactions all took place on 30 June and have been entered in the petty cash book as shown below. No entries have yet been made in the general ledger.

Petty cash book

Date	Details	Amount	Date	Details	Amount	VAT	Postages	Travel expenses	Stationery
20-4		£	20-4		£	£	£	£	£
30 Jun	Balance b/f	68.00	30 Jun	Taxi	14.88	2.48		12.40	
30 Jun	Bank	57.00	30 Jun	Copy paper	18.72	3.12			15.60
			30 Jun	Post office	11.50		11.50		
			30 Jun	Rail fare	22.35			22.35	
				Balance c/d	57.55				
		125.00			125.00	5.60	11.50	34.75	15.60

What will be the entries in the general ledger?

Select your account names from the following list: Balance b/f, Balance c/d, Bank, Copy paper, Petty cash book, Postages, Post office, Rail fare, Stationery, Taxi, Travel expenses, Value Added Tax.

General ledger

Account name	Amount £	Debit	Credit

10.8 The following petty cash book shows a number of transactions of Elliotts Limited for July 20-6. The petty cash book is kept solely as a book of prime entry.

					Petty Cash Book				**PCB35**	
Date	Details	Amount	Date	Details	Amount	VAT	Travel	Postages	Stationery	Purchases ledger
		£			£	£	£	£	£	£
1 Jul	Balance b/f	200.00								
			6 Jul	Post office	11.55			11.55		
			9 Jul	Rail fare	17.60		17.60			
			11 Jul	Envelopes	9.60	1.60			8.00	
			12 Jul	Post office	10.00			10.00		
14 Jul	T Irwin	6.25								
	(postage)									
			19 Jul	Taxi	10.08	1.68	8.40			
			22 Jul	J Clarke (PL)	18.25					18.25
			25 Jul	Marker pens	6.24	1.04			5.20	
					83.32	4.32	26.00	21.55	13.20	18.25
31 Jul	Bank	77.07								
			31 Jul	Balance c/d	200.00					
		283.32			283.32					
1 Aug	Balance b/d	200.00								

(a) You are to transfer the data from the petty cash book into the general ledger accounts (including cash book) as at 31 July 20-6. Note that a petty cash account is required.

(b) Show the entry that will be recorded in purchases ledger as at 31 July 20-6.

10.9 This is a summary of petty cash payments made by Dalbeith & Co:

Post office paid	£10.70 (no VAT)
City Taxis paid	£14.40 including VAT at 20%
Repair Shop Ltd paid	£18.80 plus VAT at 20%

    (a)   Enter the above transactions, in the order in which they are shown, in the petty cash book below.

    (b)   Total the petty cash book and show the balance carried down.

Select your entries for the Details columns from the following list: Amount, Balance b/f, Balance c/d, City Taxis, Details, Postages, Post office, Repairs, Repair Shop Ltd, Travel, VAT.

Petty cash book

Debit side		Credit side					
Details	Amount £	Details	Amount £	VAT £	Postages £	Travel £	Repairs £
Balance b/f	150.00						

10.10 Part way through the month, the petty cash account of a business had a balance of £93.30. The cash in the petty cash box was checked and the following notes and coins were present.

Notes and coins	£
4 x £10 notes	40.00
7 x £5 notes	35.00
9 x £1 coins	9.00
13 x 50p coins	6.50
10 x 10p coins	1.00
17 x 5p coins	0.85

(a) Reconcile the cash amount in the petty cash box with the balance on the petty cash account.

Amount in petty cash box	£
Balance on petty cash account	£
Difference	£

At the end of the month the cash in the petty cash box was £45.65.

(b) Complete the petty cash reimbursement below to restore the imprest amount of £175.

Petty cash reimbursement	
Date: 30.04.20-5	
Amount required to restore the cash in the petty cash box	£

11 The initial trial balance

11.1   Which **one** of the following accounts always has a credit balance?

(a) Drawings account	
(b) Sales returns account	
(c) Sales account	
(d) Office equipment account	

11.2   Which **one** of the following accounts always has a debit balance?

(a) Purchases returns account	
(b) Sales ledger control account	
(c) Capital account	
(d) Loan account	

11.3 Prepare the initial trial balance of Kate Trelawney as at 31 March 20-2. She has omitted to open a capital account. **You are to** fill in the missing figure in order to balance the trial balance.

	£
Bank loan	3,650
Purchases	23,745
Vehicle	9,500
Sales	65,034
Bank (cash at bank)	2,162
Discounts allowed	317
Purchases returns	855
Sales ledger control	7,045
Office equipment	5,450
Inventory at 1 April 20-1	4,381
Sales returns	1,624
Purchases ledger control	4,736
Expenses	32,598
Discounts received	494
Capital	?

11.4 You work as an accounts assistant for Wyvern Trading. The accounts supervisor has asked you to work on preparing an initial trial balance as at 31 December 20-8. The supervisor has given you the following list of balances to be transferred to the trial balance.

You are to place the figures in the debit or credit column, as appropriate, and to total each column.

Account name	Amount £	Debit £	Credit £
Bank (overdraft)	4,293		
Loan from bank	12,500		
Vehicles	25,500		
Inventory	10,417		
Petty cash	68		
Capital	25,794		
VAT owing to HM Revenue & Customs	1,496		
Purchases ledger control	12,794		
Purchases	104,763		
Purchases returns	2,681		
Sales ledger control	28,354		
Sales	184,267		
Sales returns	4,098		
Discounts allowed	1,312		
Discounts received	1,784		
Wages	35,961		
Telephone	3,474		
Advertising	5,921		
Insurance	3,084		
Heating and lighting	2,477		
Rent and rates	3,672		
Postages	876		
Miscellaneous expenses	545		
Drawings	15,087		
Totals	–		

11.5 You work as an accounts assistant for Highley Limited. The accounts supervisor has asked you to work on preparing an initial trial balance as at 30 June 20-1. The supervisor has given you the following list of balances to be transferred to the trial balance.

You are to place the figures in the debit or credit column, as appropriate, and to total each column.

Account name	Amount	Debit	Credit
	£	£	£
Sales	262,394		
Sales returns	2,107		
Sales ledger control	33,844		
Purchases	157,988		
Purchases returns	1,745		
Purchases ledger control	17,311		
Discounts received	1,297		
Discounts allowed	845		
Rent and rates	5,941		
Advertising	6,088		
Insurance	3,176		
Wages	48,954		
Heating and lighting	4,266		
Postages and telephone	2,107		
Miscellaneous expenses	632		
Vehicles	28,400		
Capital	48,756		
Drawings	19,354		
Office equipment	10,500		
Inventory	16,246		
Petty cash	150		
Bank (cash at bank)	3,096		
VAT owing to HM Revenue & Customs	3,721		
Loan from bank	8,470		
Totals	–		

11.6 It is important to understand the difference between capital expenditure, revenue expenditure, capital income and revenue income.

Select **one** option in each instance below to show whether the item will be capital expenditure, revenue expenditure, capital income or revenue income. You can use each classification more than once.

Item	Capital expenditure	Revenue expenditure	Capital income	Revenue income
Purchase of vehicles				
Fuel for vehicles				
Discounts received				
Receipts from sale of office equipment				
Redecoration of property				
Extension to property				
Receipts from sale of goods to credit customers				
Delivery cost of new machine				
Increase in owner's capital				
Repairs to vehicles				

Answers to chapter activities

1   The accounting system

1.1   (a)   Cash sale

1.2   (c)   The first place an entry is recorded in the accounting records

1.3   (c)   Cash and credit and other financial transactions

1.4   (b)   Customers who buy goods and services on a credit basis

1.5   A **trial balance** sets out in two columns the balances of the **ledger accounts** of a business. The **totals** of the two columns should **agree**. The debit column includes the accounts of **receivables** and the credit column includes the accounts of **payables.** This provides the **managers** of a business with important and useful financial information.

2   Financial documents for sales

2.1   **(a)**

INVOICE

PRAXIS STATIONERY
45 Jarvis Street
Mereford MR1 2GH
VAT Reg 831 8627 06

To
Dover Designs
68 Whitecliff Street, Granstow, GR3 7GH

No 1689
Date 09 07 20-3

Customer code   DO109

Delivery note no 246

Quantity	Product code	Unit price (£)	Total (£)	Net (£)	VAT (£)	Total (£)
100	BX100	4.00	400.00	320.00	64.00	384.00

(b) (c) Request a credit note for the amount of the discount (including VAT)

2.2

STATEMENT OF ACCOUNT			To Rosetti Associates
PRAXIS STATIONERY			**Date** 31 08 20-3
45 Jarvis Street, Mereford MR1 2GH			

Date	Details	Amount £	Balance outstanding £
1 August	Invoice 1748	4,567.89	4,567.89
9 August	Invoice 1778	2,457.60	7,025.49
10 August	Invoice 1783	4,678.30	11,703.79
17 August	Credit note 319	280.50	11,423.29
29 August	Cheque	4,287.39	7,135.90

2.3

Product	Customer	General Ledger Code	Customer Code
Copy paper	Britmore Ltd	GL4002	BRI45
Gel pens	Coldring Limited	GL4003	COL12
Box files	Artex Limited	GL4018	ART09
Black printer ink	Coleman Trading	GL4017	COL10
Archive storage boxes	Bristol Wholesale	GL4008	BRI25
Suspension files	Britmore Limited	GL4018	BRI45

2.4 **(c)** A credit note

2.5 **(a)** (b) £128.00

(b) (b) £768.00

3 Double-entry and the accounting equation

3.1 (c) In the ledgers

3.2 (a) Purchases ledger

3.3

	Debit	Credit
Money paid for **Purchases**	Purchases	Bank
Money received from **Sales**	Bank	Sales
Rent paid for premises used	Rent paid	Bank
Rent received for premises let	Bank	Rent received
Motor expenses paid	Motor expenses	Bank
Payment for **advertising** costs	Advertising	Bank
Stationery bill paid	Stationery	Bank
Loan received	Bank	Loan
Loan repayment made	Loan	Bank

3.4

Debit				Sales Account			Credit
Date	**Details**		**£**	**Date**	**Details**		**£**
				1 Feb	Bank		5,000
				2 Feb	Bank		7,500
				5 Feb	Bank		9,300

Debit				Purchases Account			Credit
Date	**Details**		**£**	**Date**	**Details**		**£**
1 Feb	Bank		3,500				
3 Feb	Bank		5,000				

Debit			Wages Account			Credit
Date	**Details**	**£**	**Date**	**Details**		**£**
2 Feb	Bank	2,510				

Debit			Rent Paid Account			Credit
Date	**Details**	**£**	**Date**	**Details**		**£**
4 Feb	Bank	780				

Debit			Bank Loan Account			Credit
Date	**Details**	**£**	**Date**	**Details**		**£**
			3 Feb	Bank		12,500

3.5 (a)

Statement	True	False
(a) Liabilities equals capital plus assets		✔
(b) Assets equals liabilities minus capital		✔
(c) Capital equals assets minus liabilities	✔	

(b)

Item	Asset	Liability
(a) Vehicles	✔	
(b) Bank loan		✔
(c) Money owing by trade receivables	✔	
(d) Inventory	✔	
(e) Cash	✔	
(f) VAT owing to HM Revenue & Customs		✔

3.6

Assets	Liabilities	Capital
£	£	£
50,000	0	50,000
40,000	10,000	30,000
55,200	24,950	30,250
58,980	18,220	40,760
40,320	15,980	24,340
73,350	24,760	48,590

3.7

Transaction	Debit	Credit
(a) Capital account increases		✔
(b) Liability account increases		✔
(c) Asset account decreases		✔
(d) Liability account decreases	✔	
(e) Asset account increases	✔	

3.8   (a) - (b)   Vehicles have been bought for £10,000, paid from the bank

(b) - (c)   Inventory has been bought for £6,000, paid from the bank

(c) - (d)   Inventory has been bought for £3,000, on credit from a supplier

(d) - (e)   Further vehicle bought for £8,000, paid for with £3,000 from the bank and a loan for £5,000

(e) - (f)   Owner introduces £10,000 additional capital, paid into the bank

3.9

Dr			Bank			Cr
20-4	**Details**	**£**	**20-4**	**Details**	**£**	
4 March	Capital	5,000	11 March	Purchases	375	
5 March	Bank loan	15,000	15 March	Rent	400	
7 March	Sales	670	16 March	Purchases	1,380	
18 March	Sales	430	22 March	Telephone	180	
26 March	Sales	1,320	29 March	Insurance	1,200	

Account	Date	Dr or Cr	Details	Amount £
Capital	4 March	Cr	Bank	5,000
Bank loan	5 March	Cr	Bank	15,000
Sales	7 March	Cr	Bank	670
Purchases	11 March	Dr	Bank	375
Rent	15 March	Dr	Bank	400
Purchases	16 March	Dr	Bank	1,380
Sales	18 March	Cr	Bank	430
Telephone	22 March	Dr	Bank	180
Sales	26 March	Cr	Bank	1,320
Insurance	29 March	Dr	Bank	1,200

3.10

(a)

Dr	Egret Building (Sales Ledger)				Cr
20-4	Details	£	20-4	Details	£
24 Aug	Sales	900.00	25 Aug	Sales returns	160.00
27 Aug	Sales	140.00	31 Aug	Balance c/d	1,240.00
28 Aug	Sales	360.00			
		1,400.00			1,400.00
1 Sep	Balance b/d	1,240.00			

(b)

Dr	Curtis & Curtis (Purchases Ledger)				Cr
20-4	Details	£	20-4	Details	£
31 Aug	Balance c/d	1,013.50	24 Aug	Purchases	496.00
			26 Aug	Purchases	157.50
			31 Aug	Purchases	360.00
		1,013.50			1,013.50
			1 Sep	Balance b/d	1,013.50

(c)

Dr			R & T Engineering (Purchases Ledger)			Cr
20-4	**Details**	**£**	**20-4**	**Details**		**£**
24 Aug	Purchases returns	160.00	25 Aug	Purchases		240.00
31 Aug	Balance c/d	1,140.00	28 Aug	Purchases		720.00
			31 Aug	Purchases		340.00
		1,300.00				1,300.00
			1 Sep	Balance b/d		1,140.00

(d)

Dr			Motor expenses (General Ledger)			Cr
20-4	**Details**	**£**	**20-4**	**Details**		**£**
5 Aug	Bank	150.40	31 Aug	Balance c/d		728.60
7 Aug	Bank	382.00				
9 Aug	Bank	69.30				
16 Aug	Bank	126.90				
		728.60				728.60
1 Sep	Balance b/d	728.60				

4 Accounting for sales, returns and discounts

4.1 (b) Credit note

4.2 (d) Credit note issued; sales returns day book; sales returns account; sales ledger control account; customer's account

4.3 (d) Invoice

4.4 (a)

			Sales Day Book				SDB65
Date	Details	Invoice number	Account code	Total	VAT	Net	
20-4				£	£	£	
3 Nov	Dines Stores	3592	SL086	318.00	53.00	265.00	
5 Nov	Raven Retailers Ltd	3593	SL170	402.00	67.00	335.00	
6 Nov	Meadow Golf Club	3594	SL135	210.00	35.00	175.00	
10 Nov	Wyvern Stores	3595	SL195	546.00	91.00	455.00	
11 Nov	Dines Stores	3596	SL086	348.00	58.00	290.00	
13 Nov	Teme Sports Ltd	3597	SL178	378.00	63.00	315.00	
17 Nov	Raven Retailers Ltd	3598	SL170	1,344.00	224.00	1,120.00	
19 Nov	Teme Sports Ltd	3599	SL178	990.00	165.00	825.00	
21 Nov	Dines Stores	3600	SL086	424.80	70.80	354.00	
24 Nov	Meadow Golf Club	3601	SL135	297.60	49.60	248.00	
27 Nov	Wyvern Stores	3602	SL195	627.60	104.60	523.00	
30 Nov	Totals for month			5,886.00	981.00	4,905.00	
				GL1200	GL2200	GL4100	

(b)

GENERAL LEDGER

Dr	Sales Ledger Control Account (GL1200)		Cr
20-4	£	20-4	£
30 Nov Sales Day Book SDB65	5,886.00		

Dr	Value Added Tax Account (GL2200)		Cr
20-4	£	20-4	£
		30 Nov Sales Day Book SDB65	981.00

Dr	Sales Account (GL4100)		Cr
20-4	£	20-4	£
		30 Nov Sales Day Book SDB65	4,905.00

SALES LEDGER

Dr	Dines Stores (SL086)			Cr
20-4			£	20-4 £
3 Nov Sales	SDB65	318.00		
11 Nov Sales	SDB65	348.00		
21 Nov Sales	SDB65	424.80		

Dr	Meadow Golf Club (SL135)			Cr
20-4			£	20-4 £
6 Nov Sales	SDB65	210.00		
24 Nov Sales	SDB65	297.60		

Dr	Raven Retailers Limited (SL170)			Cr
20-4			£	20-4 £
5 Nov Sales	SDB65	402.00		
17 Nov Sales	SDB65	1,344.00		

Dr	Teme Sports Limited (SL178)			Cr
20-4			£	20-4 £
13 Nov Sales	SDB65	378.00		
19 Nov Sales	SDB65	990.00		

Dr	Wyvern Stores (SL195)			Cr
20-4			£	20-4 £
10 Nov Sales	SDB65	546.00		
27 Nov Sales	SDB65	627.60		

4.5 **(a)**

	Sales Returns Day Book			SRDB22	
Date	**Details**	**Credit note number**	**Account code**	**Total**	**VAT**	**Net**
20-4				£	£	£
10 Nov	Dines Stores	831	SL086	66.00	11.00	55.00
14 Nov	Wyvern Stores	832	SL195	72.00	12.00	60.00
19 Nov	Meadow Golf Club	833	SL135	55.20	9.20	46.00
24 Nov	Teme Sports Ltd	834	SL178	152.40	25.40	127.00
28 Nov	Dines Stores	835	SL086	104.40	17.40	87.00
30 Nov	Totals for month			450.00	75.00	375.00
				GL1200	GL2200	GL4110

(b)   **GENERAL LEDGER**

Dr		**Sales Ledger Control Account** (GL1200)		Cr
20-4	£	20-4		£
30 Nov Sales Day Book SDB65 5,886.00		30 Nov Sales Returns Day Book SRDB22 450.00		

Dr		**Value Added Tax Account** (GL2200)		Cr
20-4	£	20-4		£
30 Nov Sales Returns Day Book SRDB22 75.00		30 Nov Sales Day Book SDB65 981.00		

Dr		**Sales Returns Account** (GL4110)		Cr
20-4	£	20-4		£
30 Nov Sales Returns Day Book SRDB22 375.00				

SALES LEDGER

Dr   **Dines Stores** (SL086)   Cr

20-4		£	20-4		£
3 Nov Sales	SDB65	318.00	10 Nov Sales Returns	SRDB22	66.00
11 Nov Sales	SDB65	348.00	28 Nov Sales Returns	SRDB22	104.40
21 Nov Sales	SDB65	424.80			

Dr   **Meadow Golf Club** (SL135)   Cr

20-4		£	20-4		£
6 Nov Sales	SDB65	210.00	19 Nov Sales Returns	SRDB22	55.20
24 Nov Sales	SDB65	297.60			

Dr   **Teme Sports Limited** (SL178)   Cr

20-4		£	20-4		£
13 Nov Sales	SDB65	378.00	24 Nov Sales Returns	SRDB22	152.40
19 Nov Sales	SDB65	990.00			

Dr   **Wyvern Stores** (SL195)   Cr

20-4		£	20-4		£
10 Nov Sales	SDB65	546.00	14 Nov Sales Returns	SRDB22	72.00
27 Nov Sales	SDB65	627.60			

4.6   **(a) and (b)**

Sales day book

Date 20-4	Details	Invoice number	Total £	VAT £	Net £	Sales type 1 £	Sales type 2 £
30 June	Olander Ltd	1895	1,920	320	1,600	1,600	
30 June	Boltz & Co	1896	5,040	840	4,200		4,200
30 June	Ravells	1897	576	96	480	480	
	Totals		7,536	1,256	6,280	2,080	4,200

4.7   (a)   **Sales ledger**

Account name	Amount £	Debit	Credit
Upton Ltd	2,016	✔	
Bromyards	3,408	✔	
Kempsey & Co	4,272	✔	
Fernhill plc	2,448	✔	

General ledger

Account name	Amount £	Debit	Credit
Sales	10,120		✔
Value Added Tax	2,024		✔
Sales ledger control	12,144	✔	

(b)   **Sales ledger**

Account name	Amount £	Debit	Credit
Drake & Co	336		✔
Hanbury Trading	1,008		✔

General ledger

Account name	Amount £	Debit	Credit
Sales returns	1,120	✔	
Value Added Tax	224	✔	
Sales ledger control	1,344		✔

(c)   **Sales ledger**

Account name	Amount £	Debit	Credit
Powick & Co	30		✔
Heath Trading	42		✔

General ledger

Account name	Amount £	Debit	Credit
Discounts allowed	60	✔	
Value Added Tax	12	✔	
Sales ledger control	72		✔

4.8   (a)   **General ledger**

Account name	Amount £	Debit	Credit
Discounts allowed	120	✔	
VAT	24	✔	
Sales ledger control	144		✔

(b)   **Sales ledger**

Account name	Amount £	Debit	Credit
Khan Ltd	66		✔

4.9

Sales day book

Date 20-4	Details	Invoice number	Total £	VAT £	Net £	Product S12 £	Product T12 £
30 June	Hawke Ltd	2132	360.00	60.00	300.00		300.00
30 June	T Martin	2133	450.00	75.00	375.00	375.00	
30 June	S Garner	2134	630.00	105.00	525.00	525.00	
30 June	JEC Ltd	2135	180.00	30.00	150.00		150.00
	Totals		1,620.00	270.00	1,350.00	900.00	450.00

5 Process payments from customers

5.1   (a)   Sales documention reference numbers

5.2   (c)   Same amount in words and figures, in date, signature of customer

5.3   (a)   Invoice 392 is for £690 and not for £590

(b)   Credit note 295 for £90 has not been allowed for on the remittance advice

6 Process documents from suppliers

6.1 (b) Delivery note

6.2 (c) The purchases ledger

6.3 (a) Purchases

6.4

(a) Who has supplied the chairs?

Helicon Furniture

(b) What is the problem with the consignment?

2 chairs damaged

(c) What document would be issued by the supplier to adjust the account of Praxis Stationery?

credit note

(d) Where in the supplier's accounting records would the account of Praxis Stationery be maintained?

sales ledger

6.5 Has the correct purchase price of the chairs been charged? Yes or No? YES

Has the correct discount been applied? Yes or No? NO

What would be the VAT amount charged if the invoice was correct? £288.00

What would be the total amount charged if the invoice was correct? £1,728.00

6.6 Has the correct number of tables been supplied? Yes or No? NO

Has the correct type of table been supplied? Yes or No? NO

What will be the total of the invoice on the basis of the details on the delivery note? £384.00

If a credit note were issued, what would be the total, including VAT? £76.80

7 Accounting for purchases, returns and discounts

7.1 (a) Purchases invoice

7.2 (c) Invoice received; purchases day book; purchases account; purchases ledger control account; supplier's account

7.3 (c) Debit purchases; debit VAT; credit purchases ledger control

7.4 **(a)**

	Purchases Day Book					PDB55
Date	**Details**	**Invoice number**	**Account code**	**Total**	**VAT**	**Net**
20-2				£	£	£
3 May	Malvern Manufacturing	7321	PL625	204.00	34.00	170.00
9 May	S Burston	SB745	PL530	318.00	53.00	265.00
12 May	Iley Supplies Ltd	4721	PL605	540.00	90.00	450.00
18 May	SG Enterprises	3947	PL720	990.00	165.00	825.00
23 May	S Burston	SB773	PL530	512.40	85.40	427.00
30 May	Malvern Manufacturing	7408	PL625	436.80	72.80	364.00
31 May	Totals for month			3,001.20	500.20	2,501.00
				GL2350	GL2200	GL5100

(b)   **GENERAL LEDGER**

Dr		Value Added Tax Account (GL2200)			Cr
20-2			£	20-2	£
31 May	Purchases Day Book	PDB55	500.20		

Dr		Purchases Ledger Control Account (GL2350)			Cr
20-2			£	20-2	£
				31 May Purchases Day Book PDB55	3,001.20

Dr	**Purchases Account** (GL5100)		Cr
20-2	£	20-2	£
31 May Purchases Day Book PDB55 2,501.00			

PURCHASES LEDGER

Dr	**S Burston** (PL530)		Cr
20-2	£	20-2	£
		9 May Purchases PDB55	318.00
		23 May Purchases PDB55	512.40

Dr	**Iley Supplies Limited** (PL605)		Cr
20-2	£	20-2	£
		12 May Purchases PDB55	540.00

Dr	**Malvern Manufacturing** (PL625)		Cr
20-2	£	20-2	£
		3 May Purchases PDB55	204.00
		30 May Purchases PDB55	436.80

Dr	**SG Enterprises** (PL720)		Cr
20-2	£	20-2	£
		18 May Purchases PDB55	990.00

7.5   **(a)**

Purchases Returns Day Book						PRDB14
Date	**Details**	**Credit note number**	**Account code**	**Total**	**VAT**	**Net**
20-2				£	£	£
11 May	Malvern Manufacturing	CN345	PL625	84.00	14.00	70.00
17 May	Iley Supplies Ltd	CN241	PL605	102.00	17.00	85.00
24 May	SG Enterprises	85	PL720	30.00	5.00	25.00
31 May	S Burston	SB95	PL530	66.00	11.00	55.00
31 May	Totals for month			282.00	47.00	235.00
				GL2350	GL2200	GL5110

(b)   GENERAL LEDGER

Dr	Value Added Tax Account (GL2200)		Cr
20-2	£	20-2	£
31 May Purchases Day Book PDB55	500.20	31 May Purchases Returns Day Book PRDB14	47.00

Dr	Purchases Ledger Control Account (GL2350)		Cr
20-2	£	20-2	£
31 May Purchases Returns Day Book PRDB14	282.00	31 May Purchases Day Book PDB55	3,001.20

Dr	Purchases Returns Account (GL5110)		Cr
20-2	£	20-2	£
		31 May Purchases Returns Day Book PRDB14	235.00

PURCHASES LEDGER

Dr	S Burston (PL530)			Cr
20-2	£	20-2		£
31 May Purchases Returns PRDB14	66.00	9 May Purchases 23 May Purchases	PDB55 PDB55	318.00 512.40

Dr		**Iley Supplies Limited** (PL605)		Cr
20-2	£	20-2		£
17 May Purchases Returns		12 May Purchases	PDB55	540.00
PRDB14	102.00			

Dr		**Malvern Manufacturing** (PL625)		Cr
20-2	£	20-2		£
11 May Purchases Returns		3 May Purchases	PDB55	204.00
PRDB14	84.00	30 May Purchases	PDB55	436.80

Dr		**SG Enterprises** (PL720)		Cr
20-2	£	20-2		£
24 May Purchases Returns		18 May Purchases	PDB55	990.00
PRDB14	30.00			

7.6 Purchases day book

Date 20-4	Details	Invoice number	Total £	VAT £	Net £	Purchases type 1 £	Purchases type 2 £
30 June	King & Co	K641	2,016	336	1,680		1,680
30 June	Rossingtons	2129	3,072	512	2,560	2,560	
30 June	Moniz Ltd	M/149	2,208	368	1,840		1,840
	Totals		7,296	1,216	6,080	2,560	3,520

7.7   **(a)**   **Purchases ledger**

Account name	Amount £	Debit	Credit
H & L Ltd	6,528		✔
Sperrin & Co	2,208		✔
Hickmores	4,608		✔
Marklew plc	1,104		✔

General ledger

Account name	Amount £	Debit	Credit
Purchases	12,040	✔	
Value Added Tax	2,408	✔	
Purchases ledger control	14,448		✔

(b)   **Purchases ledger**

Account name	Amount £	Debit	Credit
Marcer Transport	624	✔	
Schuller Ltd	432	✔	

General ledger

Account name	Amount £	Debit	Credit
Purchases returns	880		✔
Value Added Tax	176		✔
Purchases ledger control	1,056	✔	

(c)   **Purchases ledger**

Account name	Amount £	Debit	Credit
DDE & Co	18	✔	
Transpo Ltd	24	✔	

General ledger

Account name	Amount £	Debit	Credit
Discounts received	35		✔
Value Added Tax	7		✔
Purchases ledger control	42	✔	

7.8 **(a)** **General ledger**

Account name	Amount £	Debit	Credit
Discounts received	195		✔
VAT	39		✔
Purchases ledger control	234	✔	

(b) **Purchases ledger**

Account name	Amount £	Debit	Credit
Hussain plc	102	✔	

7.9

Purchases day book

Date 20-4	Details	Invoice number	Total £	VAT £	Net £	Product S12 £	Product T12 £
30 June	Lyster Ltd	4681	1,200.00	200.00	1000.00	1,000.00	
30 June	T England	6234	432.00	72.00	360.00		360.00
30 June	Mere Ltd	1634	1,080.00	180.00	900.00		900.00
30 June	J Mehta	8561	480.00	80.00	400.00	400.00	
	Totals		3,192.00	532.00	2,660.00	1,400.00	1,260.00

8 Prepare payments to suppliers

8.1 (a) An increase in the total amount owing shown on the statement of account

8.2 (c) Purchase invoices, purchase credit notes, total amount owing

8.3 (b) Will reduce the total amount shown as owing on the statement of account

8.4 **(a)** Cheque for £1,000
(b) Invoice 790
(c) £360

8.5 **(a)** (b) Without a cheque to A Strauss & Co
(b) (c) 30 April
(c) (b) Invoice 2461, invoice 2479, credit note CN105
(d) (c) £3,640

9 Cash book

9.1 (c) BACS transfer from a trade receivable for £1,950

9.2 (a) **Sales ledger**

Account name	Amount £	Debit	Credit
Delta & Co	325		✔
Boscawen Ltd	1,540		✔

(b) **General ledger**

Account name	Amount £	Debit	Credit
Sales ledger control	325		✔
Sales ledger control	1,540		✔

(c) **General ledger**

Account name	Amount £	Debit	Credit
Wages	1,265	✔	
Office equipment	1,968	✔	

9.3   **(a)**   **Sales ledger**

Account name	Amount £	Debit	Credit
Smithsons Ltd	2,325		✔
Egerton & Co	425		✔

(b)   **General ledger**

Account name	Amount £	Debit	Credit
Sales ledger control	*2,750		✔
Wages	1,175	✔	
Rent	1,200	✔	
Stationery	120	✔	

*£2,325 + £425

9.4 **(a)** True

(b) False – the balance b/d of £201 on 1 October shows that, according to the cash book, there is a bank overdraft.

(c)

GENERAL LEDGER

Dr			Sales Account			Cr
20-1			£	20-1		£
				30 Sep Cash	CB68	88

Dr			Sales Ledger Control Account			Cr
20-1			£	20-1		£
				30 Sep Bank	CB68	1,580

Dr			Purchases Ledger Control Account			Cr
20-1			£	20-1		£
30 Sep Bank	CB68	1,940				

Dr			Purchases Account			Cr
20-1			£	20-1		£
30 Sep Bank	CB68	192				

Dr			General Expenses Account			Cr
20-1			£	20-1		£
30 Sep Cash	CB68	128				

Dr			Wages Account			Cr
20-1			£	20-1		£
30 Sep Bank	CB68	1,254				

Dr			Office Equipment Account			Cr
20-1			£	20-1		£
30 Sep Bank	CB68	1,440				

(d)

SALES LEDGER

Dr			Albany Limited			Cr
20-1		£	20-1			£
			30 Sep	Bank	CB68	1,580

PURCHASES LEDGER

Dr			Nelson Stores			Cr
20-1			£	20-1		£
30 Sep	Bank	CB68	1,940			

9.5

Cash Book

Dr

Date 20-7	Details	Cash £	Bank £
3 Aug	Balance b/d	286	
4 Aug	Sales	334	
5 Aug	Murphy Ltd		1,475
10 Aug	Balance c/d		3,870
		620	5,345
11 Aug	Balance b/d	140	

Cr

Date 20-7	Details	Cash £	Bank £
3 Aug	Balance b/d		3,472
3 Aug	Rent		760
8 Aug	Rates		223
8 Aug	JJ Supplies		490
10 Aug	Drawings		400
10 Aug	Wages	480	
10 Aug	Balance c/d	140	
		620	5,345
11 Aug	Balance b/d		3,870

Tutorial note: prompt payment discount for the transactions on 5 August and 8 August is not recorded in the cash book; instead, a credit note will be issued by the supplier to the customer (see Chapters 4 and 7).

9.6

Cash Book

Dr | | | | | | | Cr

Date 20-3	Details	Cash £	Bank £	Date 20-3	Details	Cash £	Bank £
1 Mar	Balance b/d	200		1 Mar	Balance b/d		1,898
6 Mar	Court Ltd		1,236	2 Mar	Lindum Supplies		254
13 Mar	H Sweeney BACS		1,696	11 Mar	Rent		550
14 Mar	Sales	639		23 Mar	Wages	655	
24 Mar	Sales	786		26 Mar	Wyvern Council SO		195
28 Mar	Mills & Co Ltd BACS		477	27 Mar	Bank interest		45
				31 Mar	Balance c/d	970	467
		1,625	3,409			1,625	3,409
1 Apr	Balances b/d	970	467				

9.7   (c)   Debit card payment to a trade payable for £940

9.8   **(a)**, **(c)** and **(d)** are true; **(b)** is false.

9.9   **(a)**   **Cash book – credit side**

Details	Cash £	Bank £	VAT £	Trade payables £	Cash purchases £	Stationery expenses £
Balance b/f						
Clark & Co	48		8		40	
T Kinnear	192		32		160	
Gaskin Ltd		1,690		1,690		
Bristow Stationery		144	24			120
Roussouw & Co		1,140		1,140		
Totals	240	2,974	64	2,830	200	120

(b)   **Cash book – debit side**

Details	Cash £	Bank £	Trade receivables £
Balance b/f	642	1,022	
Passmores		455	455
S McNulty		833	833
Totals	642	2,310	1,288

(c)   £402

(d)   £664

(e)   Credit

9.10 (a)

Cash book – credit side

Details	Cash £	Bank £	VAT £	Trade payables £	Cash purchases £	Other expenses £
Balance b/f		2,417				
Mary Wallbank	192		32		160	
Wenton Council		425				425
Sanders plc		600		600		
J Panas		672		672		
Totals	192	4,114	32	1,272	160	425

(b)

Cash book – debit side

Details	Cash £	Bank £	Trade receivables £	Other income £
Balance b/f	208			
LFJ plc		1,685	1,685	
Wragg Ltd		2,135	2,135	
Nikki Shah	200			200
Totals	408	3,820	3,820	200

(c) £216

(d) −£294

(e)

Account name	Amount	Debit	Credit
Wragg Ltd	2,135		✔

10 Petty cash book

10.1   (c) The petty cash float is restored to the same amount for the beginning of each week or month

10.2   (b) Debit petty cash £108; credit bank £108

10.3   **(a)** is false; the others are true

10.4   (c)   £139.90

10.5   (a)   £72.77

10.6   **General ledger**

Account name	Amount £	Debit	Credit
Petty cash book	110	✔	
Bank	110		✔

10.7   **General ledger**

Account name	Amount £	Debit	Credit
VAT	5.60	✔	
Postages	11.50	✔	
Travel expenses	34.75	✔	
Stationery	15.60	✔	
Bank	57.00		✔

10.8 **(a)**

GENERAL LEDGER

Dr		Value Added Tax Account		Cr
20-6			£	20-6	£
31 Jul	Petty cash book	PCB35	4.32	

Dr		Travel Account		Cr
20-6			£	20-6	£
31 Jul	Petty cash book	PCB35	26.00	

Dr		Postages Account		Cr
20-6			£	20-6	£
31 Jul	Petty cash book	PCB35	21.55	14 Jul	Petty cash book	PCB35	6.25

Dr		Stationery Account		Cr
20-6			£	20-6	£
31 Jul	Petty cash book	PCB35	13.20	

Dr		Purchases Ledger Control Account		Cr
20-6			£	20-6	£
31 Jul	Petty cash book	PCB35	18.25	

Dr		Petty Cash Account		Cr
20-6			£	20-6	£
1 Jul	Balance b/d		200.00	31 Jul	Petty cash book	PCB35	83.32
31 Jul	Petty cash book	PCB35	6.25	31 Jul	Balance c/d		200.00
31 Jul	Bank	CB	77.07		
			283.32				283.32
1 Aug	Balance b/d		200.00		

Dr		Cash Book		Cr
20-6			Bank	20-6	Bank
				31 Jul	Petty cash	PCB35	77.07

(b)

PURCHASES LEDGER

Dr		J Clarke		Cr
20-6			£	20-6	£
22 Jul	Petty cash book	PCB35	18.25	

10.9 (a) and (b)

Petty cash book

Debit side		Credit side					
Details	Amount £	Details	Amount £	VAT £	Postages £	Travel £	Repairs £
Balance b/f	150.00	Post office	10.70		10.70		
		City Taxis	14.40	2.40		12.00	
		Repair Shop Ltd	22.56	3.76			18.80
		Balance c/d	102.34				
	150.00		150.00	6.16	10.70	12.00	18.80

10.10 (a)

Amount in petty cash box	£92.35
Balance on petty cash account	£93.30
Difference	£ 0.95

(b)

Petty cash reimbursement	
Date: 30.04.20-5	
Amount required to restore the cash in the petty cash box	£129.35

11 The initial trial balance

11.1 (c) Sales account

11.2 (b) Sales ledger control account

11.3

Trial balance of Kate Trelawney as at 31 March 20-2

Name of account	Dr £	Cr £
Bank loan		3,650
Purchases	23,745	
Vehicle	9,500	
Sales		65,034
Bank (cash at bank)	2,162	
Discounts allowed	317	
Purchases returns		855
Sales ledger control	7,045	
Office equipment	5,450	
Inventory at 1 April 20-1	4,381	
Sales returns	1,624	
Purchases ledger control		4,736
Expenses	32,598	
Discounts received		494
Capital *(missing figure)*		12,053
	86,822	86,822

11.4

Account name	Amount £	Debit £	Credit £
Bank (overdraft)	4,293		4,293
Loan from bank	12,500		12,500
Vehicles	25,500	25,500	
Inventory	10,417	10,417	
Petty cash	68	68	
Capital	25,794		25,794
VAT owing to HM Revenue & Customs	1,496		1,496
Purchases ledger control	12,794		12,794
Purchases	104,763	104,763	
Purchases returns	2,681		2,681
Sales ledger control	28,354	28,354	
Sales	184,267		184,267
Sales returns	4,098	4,098	
Discounts allowed	1,312	1,312	
Discounts received	1,784		1,784
Wages	35,961	35,961	
Telephone	3,474	3,474	
Advertising	5,921	5,921	
Insurance	3,084	3,084	
Heating and lighting	2,477	2,477	
Rent and rates	3,672	3,672	
Postages	876	876	
Miscellaneous expenses	545	545	
Drawings	15,087	15,087	
Totals	–	245,609	245,609

11.5

Account name	Amount £	Debit £	Credit £
Sales	262,394		262,394
Sales returns	2,107	2,107	
Sales ledger control	33,844	33,844	
Purchases	157,988	157,988	
Purchases returns	1,745		1,745
Purchases ledger control	17,311		17,311
Discounts received	1,297		1,297
Discounts allowed	845	845	
Rent and rates	5,941	5,941	
Advertising	6,088	6,088	
Insurance	3,176	3,176	
Wages	48,954	48,954	
Heating and lighting	4,266	4,266	
Postages and telephone	2,107	2,107	
Miscellaneous expenses	632	632	
Vehicles	28,400	28,400	
Capital	48,756		48,756
Drawings	19,354	19,354	
Office equipment	10,500	10,500	
Inventory	16,246	16,246	
Petty cash	150	150	
Bank (cash at bank)	3,096	3,096	
VAT owing to HM Revenue & Customs	3,721		3,721
Loan from bank	8,470		8,470
Totals	–	343,694	343,694

11.6

Item	Capital expenditure	Revenue expenditure	Capital income	Revenue income
Purchase of vehicles	✔			
Fuel for vehicles		✔		
Discounts received				✔
Receipts from sale of office equipment			✔	
Redecoration of property		✔		
Extension to property	✔			
Receipts from sale of goods to credit customers				✔
Delivery cost of new machine	✔			
Increase in owner's capital			✔	
Repairs to vehicles		✔		

Practice
assessment 1

This practice assessment contains 10 tasks and you should attempt to complete every task.

Each task is independent. You will not need to refer to your answers to previous tasks. Where the date is relevant, it is given in the task data.

The tasks are set in different business situations where the following apply:

- All businesses use a manual bookkeeping system.

- Double-entry takes place in the general ledger. Individual accounts of trade receivables and trade payables are kept in the sales and purchases ledgers as subsidiary accounts.

- The cash book and petty cash book should be treated as part of the double-entry system unless the task instructions state otherwise.

- The VAT rate is 20%.

Task 1

(a) You receive the purchase order shown below and are required to complete the following details on the invoice on the next page. The date is 13 May 20-X.

- the goods total before trade discount
- the discount amount
- the net amount after trade discount
- the VAT amount (VAT @ 20%)
- the invoice total

G Finsey Limited		PURCHASE ORDER	
Unit 23			
Broadfield Estate			
Broadfield			
BR6 8YU			

J Bark Trading Ltd	purchase order no	47609
35 High Road	date	10 05 20-X
Wonsbury		
WO6 5FG		

Product code	Quantity	Description
36119	150	30mm Blue Grinder, less trade discount @ 10%

AUTHORISED signature.......*A W Bolt*.......date...*10/05/20-x*...

INVOICE

J Bark Trading Limited
35 High Road, Wonsbury, WO6 5FG
Tel 01908 765314 Fax 01908 765951 Email sales@barkertrading.co.uk
VAT Reg GB 0745 4672 76

invoice to

G Finsey Limited **Unit 23 Broadfield Estate** **Broadfield** **BR6 8YU**	invoice no 787923 account 3993 your reference 47609 date/tax point **13 May 20-X**

Product code	Description	Quantity	Price	Unit	Total	Discount @10%	Net
36119	30mm Blue grinder	150	1.50	each			

terms
Net monthly
Carriage paid
E & OE

Goods total	
VAT	
TOTAL	

(b) Enter the appropriate amounts from the completed invoice in Task 1 (a) in the sales day book shown below.

Sales day book

Date	Details	Invoice number	Total £	VAT £	Net £

(c) A BACS payment for £1,982.00 has been received from Malvern Fashions who incorrectly state that the amount is in full settlement of their account balance as at 31 March 20-X.

The customer's account in the sales ledger is shown below.

Dr				Malvern Fashions		Cr
Date 20-X	**Details**	**Amount** £	**Date** 20-X	**Details**		**Amount** £
1 Mar	Balance b/f	980	3 Mar	Credit note 755		159
13 Mar	Invoice 3431	1,752	6 Mar	Bank		821
16 Mar	Invoice 3478	450	21 Mar	Credit note 761		220
22 Mar	Invoice 3493	135	23 Mar	Credit note 769		120
27 Mar	Invoice 3510	1,650				

You are to calculate the correct up-to-date balance of the Malvern Fashions account as shown in the sales ledger account above and then indicate with a tick in the right-hand column of the table below which three transactions are still outstanding.

Balance b/f	
Credit note 755	
Bank	
Invoice 3431	
Invoice 3478	
Credit note 761	
Invoice 3493	
Credit note 769	
Invoice 3510	

(d)   R Strauss Limited has just introduced to its customers a prompt payment discount of 5% for payment within 10 days of the invoice date. Elektra Travel receives the invoice below and pays in full within 7 days. R Strauss Travel Goods then sends a credit note to Elektra Travel for the amount to be refunded.

The total amount of the refund on the credit note (including VAT @ 20%) is £ ⬚

R STRAUSS TRAVEL GOODS   INVOICE

65 Floral Road
Tooting Bec
London SW16 7RU
Tel 0207 765100 Fax 0207 765101 Email sales@rstrauss.co.uk VAT Reg GB 0745 3424 90

invoice to

Elektra Travel Unit 3 Quinns Road Estate Twickenham London TW1 9GG	

invoice no	94456
account	EL172
your reference	928470
date/tax point	30 June 20-X

Product code	Description	Quantity	Price	Unit	Total	20% Trade Discount	Net
8442	Vienna travel pack	10	25.95	each	259.50	51.90	207.60

terms
Net monthly
Prompt payment discount of 5% for payment within 10 days
Carriage paid
E & OE

Goods total	207.60
VAT	41.52
TOTAL	249.12

Task 2

(a)   The purchase order and invoice shown below relate to goods ordered and received by James Plant Garden Centre. Compare the details on the two documents and answer the question on the next page.

James Plant Garden Centre   **PURCHASE ORDER**

The Nursery
Broadfield Road
Bloomfield
BR6 8YU

Gabriel Oak Garden Supplies Ltd	purchase order no	84466
Northwick Farm	date	06 07 20-X
Northwick		
BR8 2FG		

Product code	Quantity	Description
4944	10	Jacquemontii Silver Birch tree @ £35.00 less 20% trade discount

AUTHORISED   signature........*J K Plant*..date..*6/07/20-x*....

INVOICE   **Gabriel Oak Garden Supplies Limited**

Northwick Farm
Northwick
BR8 2FG

invoice to

James Plant Garden Centre	invoice no	787923
The Nursery	account	3993
Broadfield Road	your reference	8466
Bloomfield BR8 2FG	date/tax point	08 July 20-X

Product code	Description	Quantity	Price	Unit	Total	Discount @10%	Net
4494	Silver Birch tree (Jacquemontii)	20	30.00	each	600.00	60.00	540.00

terms

Net monthly

Carriage paid

E & OE

Goods total	540.00
VAT	108.00
TOTAL	648.00

Task 2 (a) continued

Compare the purchase order and the invoice on the previous page.

Identify the discrepancies on the invoice and link the boxes below with lines. The left-hand column of boxes sets out where on the invoice errors could take place and the right-hand column of boxes describes the types of error that could occur.

purchase order number

product code

figure incorrect on invoice

amount of goods ordered

quantity incorrect

trade discount

price incorrect

price quoted

(b) The invoice shown at the bottom of the page has been issued by Gabriel Oak Garden Supplies.

Record the details from the invoice in the appropriate day book operated by Gabriel Oak Garden Supplies. Choose between:

- Discounts allowed day book
- Discounts received day book
- Purchases day book
- Purchases returns day book
- Sales day book
- Sales returns day book

Name of day book:

Date 20-X	Details	Invoice number	Total £	VAT £	Net £

INVOICE **Gabriel Oak Garden Supplies Limited**

Northwick Farm
Northwick
BR8 2FG

invoice to

James Plant Garden Centre
The Nursery
Broadfield Road
Bloomfield BR8 2FG

invoice no	787963
account	3993
your reference	8491
date/tax point	25 July 20-X

Product code	Description	Quantity	Price	Unit	Total	Discount @10%	Net
4494	Rhododendron (Red Spirit)	5	20.00	each	100.00	10.00	90.00

terms

Net monthly

Carriage paid

E & OE

Goods total	90.00
VAT	18.00
TOTAL	108.00

Task 3

(a)   Lumino Lighting always checks statements of account when they are received from suppliers. The statements have to be carefully checked because they may contain purchases which have not yet been received and recorded in Lumino Lighting's purchases ledger. Set out below are:

–   the statement of account received from Sparks Electrical Supplies

–   the supplier account of Sparks Electrical Supplies in the purchases ledger of Lumino Lighting

You are to:

•   Compare the entries on the two documents to identify amounts which appear on only one of the documents.

•   Tick the boxes next to the statement of account for the three items which are missing from the supplier account in Lumino Lighting's purchases ledger and so should not be paid.

STATEMENT OF ACCOUNT
Sparks Electrical supplies
45 Jarvis Street, Mereford MR1 2GH

To Lumino Lighting
Date 30 06 20-X

Date 20-X	Invoice/credit note number	Details	Amount £	✔
1 Jul	CN1073	Goods returned	200	
8 Jul	INV1780	Goods	590	
14 Jul	INV1810	Goods	10,250	
21 Jul	CN1090	Goods returned	195	
24 Jul	INV1975	Goods	1,720	
30 Jul	INV2006	Goods	710	

Sparks Electrical Supplies

Date 20-X	Details	Amount £	Date 20-X	Details	Amount £
1 Jul	CN1073	200	1 Jul	Balance b/f	15,620
2 Jul	Bank	15,620	14 Jul	INV1810	10,250
			24 Jul	INV1975	1,720

(b)   The amount paid will be £ _____

(c)   Cotswold Stone Limited has supplied Barry Builders & Co with faulty paving stones. They have agreed to issue a credit note to provide a refund. Set out below are the account of Cotswold Stone Limited in the purchases ledger of Barry Builders & Co and the credit note issued. The credit note has not yet been entered into the purchases ledger account.

Cotswold Stone Limited

Date 20-X	Details	Amount £	Date 20-X	Details	Amount £
1 Jul	Bank	5,460	1 Jul	Balance b/f	6,540
2 Jul	Credit note 753	673	4 Jul	Invoice 1810	2,250
			5 Jul	Invoice 1818	3,610
			6 Jul	Invoice 1824	645

CREDIT NOTE   Cotswold Stone Limited

The Quarry
Doddington
GL4 8HG

credit to

Barry Builders & Co
Pershore Road
Linkborough
WR6 9FG

credit note no	2793
account	BB170
your reference	7612
date/tax point	9 July 20-X

Product code	Description	Quantity	Price	Unit	Total	Discount @20%	Net Total
FS944	Cotswold Flagstone	5	45.00	pack	225.00	45.00	180.00

reason for credit
Slabs damaged on receipt - refund given

Goods total	180.00
VAT	36.00
TOTAL	216.00

You are asked to calculate the amount that will be owing to Cotswold Stone Limited by Barry Builders and Co after the credit note has been entered into the purchases ledger of Barry Builders & Co.

The amount due is £ ☐

(d) The two invoices on this and the next page offer a prompt payment discount for settlement within a certain period of time indicated in the invoice terms.

INVOICE

No 1689

SHARP STATIONERY LTD
45 Jarvis Street
Mereford MR1 2GH
VAT Reg 831 8627 06

Date 06 08 20-X

To
Dover Recruitment
68 Whitecliff Street, Granstow, GR3 7GH

Product code	Description	Quantity	Price	Unit	Total	Discount @20%	Net Total
BF7264	Box Files	100	5.00	each	500.00	100.00	400.00

terms

Net monthly
Prompt payment discount of 2% for payment within 14 days of invoice date
E & OE

Goods total	400.00
VAT	80.00
TOTAL	480.00

The amount that will be paid if the prompt payment discount is taken will be:

(a)	£480.00	
(b)	£392.00	
(c)	£470.40	

Tick the appropriate box.

The date by which the amount will have to be paid if the prompt payment discount is taken will be:

(a)	31 August	
(b)	13 August	
(c)	20 August	

Tick the appropriate box.

(d)   continued

INVOICE   **No** 1689

FELLOWES DRY CLEANING   **Date** 09 08 20-X

45 Jarvis Street
Mereford MR1 2GH
VAT Reg 831 8632 01

To
R Whittington, Solicitors
21 High Street, Beresford, BE3 iGH

Product code	Description	Quantity	Price	Unit	Total	Discount @10%	Net Total
S4642	Suit dry cleaning	20	15.00	each	300.00	30.00	270.00

terms

Net monthly
Prompt payment discount of 5% for payment within 7 days
of invoice date
E & OE

Goods total	270.00
VAT	54.00
TOTAL	324.00

The amount that will be paid if the prompt payment discount is taken will be:

(a)	£324.00	
(b)	£307.80	
(c)	£312.90	

Tick the appropriate box.

The date by which the amount will have to be paid if the prompt payment discount is taken will be:

(a)	16 August	
(b)	19 August	
(c)	31 August	

Tick the appropriate box.

Task 4

The three amounts shown below have been paid to suppliers and are ready to be entered in the cash book.

Cash purchases listing

Suppliers paid in cash	Net £	VAT £	Gross £
Alvington Supplies	150	30	180

Trade payables listing

Credit suppliers paid by BACS	Amount paid £
Halwell Ltd	2,106
Frogmore & Co	1,164

(a) Make the necessary entries in the cash book and total each column.

Select your entries for the Details column from the following list: Alvington Supplies, Bank, Cash, Cash purchases, Frogmore & Co, Halwell Ltd, Trade payables, VAT.

Cash book – credit side

Details	Cash £	Bank £	VAT £	Trade payables £	Cash purchases £
Balance b/f		4,720			
Totals					

(b) The debit side of the cash book shows the cash balance brought forward at the beginning of the week was £250 and a further £412 has been received during the week.

Using your answers to (a), calculate the cash balance.

£ [   ]

(c) The debit side of the cash book shows the total amount of money banked during the week was £5,341.

Using your answers to (a), calculate the bank balance. Use a minus sign if your calculations indicate an overdrawn bank balance, eg –123.

£ [   ]

Task 5

The two petty cash vouchers below are ready to be entered into the partially completed petty cash book.

petty cash voucher		159
date	*30 June 20-6*	

	£	p
A4 paper	20	00
VAT at 20%	4	00
Total	24	00

petty cash voucher		160
date	*30 June 20-6*	

	£	p
Window cleaning	10	00
VAT is not applicable		
	10	00

(a) Complete the petty cash book by:

- Entering both transactions into the petty cash book below.

  Select your entry for the Details column from the following list: Balance b/f, Balance c/d, Cleaning, Paper, Office expenses, Postage stamps, VAT, Window cleaning.

- Totalling the petty cash book and inserting the balance carried down at 30 June.

Petty cash book

Date 20-6	Details	Amount £	Date 20-6	Details	Amount £	VAT £	Office expenses £	Cleaning £
15 June	Balance b/f	47.80	20 June	Postage stamps	40.00		40.00	
15 June	Cash from bank	77.20						
	Total			Totals				

(b) What will be the amount of cash withdrawn from the bank to restore the imprest level of £125.00?

£ [   ]

Task 6

These are the totals of the discounts allowed day book at the end of the month.

Discounts allowed day book

Details	Total £	VAT £	Net £
Totals	384	64	320

(a) What will be the entries in the general ledger?

Select your account names from the following list: Discounts allowed, Discounts received, Purchases, Purchases ledger control, Purchases returns, Sales, Sales ledger control, Sales returns, VAT.

General ledger

Account name	Amount £	Debit	Credit

One of the entries in the discounts allowed day book is for a credit note sent to Modbury Ltd for £65 plus VAT.

(b) What will be the entry in the sales ledger?

Select your account name from the following list: Discounts allowed, Discounts received, Modbury Ltd, Purchases, Purchases ledger control, Purchases returns, Sales, Sales ledger control, Sales returns, VAT.

Sales ledger

Account name	Amount £	Debit	Credit

Task 7

These are the totals of the cash book at the end of the month.

Cash book

Cash £	Bank £	VAT £	Trade receivables £	Cash sales £	Cash £	Bank £	VAT £	Trade payables £	Cash purchases £
335	12,790	–	12,790	–	335	12,790	51	9,105	255

What will be the entries in the general ledger?

Select your account names from the following list: Bank, Cash, Cash purchases, Cash sales, Purchases ledger control, Sales ledger control, Trade payables, Trade receivables, VAT.

General ledger

Account name	Amount £	Debit	Credit

Task 8

The following two accounts are in the general ledger at close of day on 30 September.

Loan from bank

Date 20-6	Details	Amount £	Date 20-6	Details	Amount £
15 Sep	Bank	1,340	1 Sep	Balance b/f	18,695
			30 Sep	Bank	7,500

Motor vehicles

Date 20-6	Details	Amount £	Date 20-6	Details	Amount £
1 Sep	Balance b/f	15,084	25 Sep	Journal	350
15 Sep	Bank	7,296			

(a) What will be the balance brought down at 1 October on each account?

Account name	Balance b/d at 1 October £	Debit	Credit
Loan from bank			
Motor vehicles			

The following account is in the purchases ledger at the close of day on 30 September.

(b) Complete the account below by:

- Inserting the balance carried down together with date and details.
- Inserting the totals.
- Inserting the balance brought down together with date and details.

Thomas Thomson

Date 20-6	Details	Amount £	Date 20-6	Details	Amount £
20 Sep	Bank	3,089	1 Sep	Balance b/f	6,241
25 Sep	Credit note C459	547	15 Sep	Invoice 4731	1,468
	Total			Total	

Task 9

Below are two general ledger accounts and a partially completed trial balance.

Complete the trial balance by:

· Transferring the balances of the two general ledger accounts to the debit or credit column of the trial balance.

· Entering the amounts shown against each of the other account names into the debit or credit column of the trial balance.

· Totalling both columns of the trial balance.

Do not enter figures with decimal places in this task and do not enter a zero in unused column cells.

Sales

Date 20-6	Details	Amount £	Date 20-6	Details	Amount £
30 April	Journal	420	1 April	Balance b/f	64,159
30 April	Balance c/d	79,085	30 April	Sales ledger control	15,346
		79,505			79,505

Purchases

Date 20-6	Details	Amount £	Date 20-6	Details	Amount £
1 April	Balance b/f	30,382	30 April	Balance c/d	40,029
30 April	Purchases ledger control	9,647			
		40,029			40,029

Trial balance as at 30 April

Account name	Amount £	Debit £	Credit £
Sales			
Purchases			
Administration expenses	4,351		
Loan from bank	6,400		
Office equipment	15,050		
Selling expenses	4,965		
Sales ledger control	18,273		
Purchases ledger control	12,692		
Wages	28,518		
Capital	13,009		
Totals			

Task 10

A business has allocated a supplier account code to each supplier in the purchases ledger, as shown below. The code is made up of the first four letters of the supplier's name, followed by the number of the ledger page. The ledger pages are set out in alphabetical order.

Supplier name	Supplier account code
Ballard Limited	BALL02
Daley & Son	DALE04
Hamer Lighting	HAME08
Longstaff & Co	LONG19
Schwindler Importers	SCHW19
Wallace Consultancy	WALL23
Warren Ltd	WARR23

Two new supplier accounts shown below have been added to the purchases ledger and need to be allocated a supplier account code.

(a) Insert the relevant account codes for each supplier.

Wesley Fasteners Ltd   **Account code** [   ]

Date 20-X	Details	Amount £	Date 20-X	Details	Amount £
			6 Jul	Invoice 6252	1,233

Sansome Meats   **Account code** [   ]

Date 20-X	Details	Amount £	Date 20-X	Details	Amount £
			6 Jul	Invoice 6253	963

A customer has been offered a prompt payment discount for payment within 10 days.

(b)   Show what **two** actions should be taken by the supplier if the customer takes the discount and pays within 10 days.

(a) Record the amount received in the cash book and ledgers	
(b) Ask the customer to amend the amount on the invoice	
(c) Reduce the VAT amount on the invoice by the discount percentage	
(d) Issue a credit note for the discount taken (including VAT)	

A company that manufactures promotional mugs has the following assets and liabilities:

Assets and liabilities	£
Property	150,000
Computer equipment	40,000
Inventories	12,920
Bank overdraft	24,117
Trade payables	18,920
Trade receivables	21,710

(c)   Calculate the total assets and liabilities for the accounting equation and insert the appropriate figures below.

Assets £	Liabilities £	Capital £

(d) The transactions set out below on the left have taken place within a large firm of Accountants.

Decide whether each transaction will be classified as:

- capital income
- revenue income
- capital expenditure
- revenue expenditure

Draw a line between each transaction description on the left and the appropriate classification of income or expenditure set out on the right. You may need to use a classification more than once.

The sale of the firm's Birmingham office	**CAPITAL INCOME**
The purchase of an office in London	
Staff wages	**CAPITAL EXPENDITURE**
Interest received on bank deposits	**REVENUE INCOME**
Insurance costs	
Clients' fees received	**REVENUE EXPENDITURE**

Practice assessment 2

This practice assessment contains 10 tasks and you should attempt to complete every task.

Each task is independent. You will not need to refer to your answers to previous tasks. Where the date is relevant, it is given in the task data.

The tasks are set in different business situations where the following apply:

- All businesses use a manual bookkeeping system.

- Double-entry takes place in the general ledger. Individual accounts of trade receivables and trade payables are kept in the sales and purchases ledgers as subsidiary accounts.

- The cash book and petty cash book should be treated as part of the double-entry system unless the task instructions state otherwise.

- The VAT rate is 20%.

Task 1

(a)   You receive the purchase order shown below and are required to complete the following details on the invoice on the next page. The date is 19 April 20-X.

- the goods total before trade discount
- the discount amount
- the net amount after trade discount
- the VAT amount (VAT @ 20%)
- the invoice total

W Walton Trading Ltd		**PURCHASE ORDER**	
Unit 19			
Mortella Business Park			
Broadfield			
BR3 7VB			
E Ragle Ltd 56 Crown East Drive Lower Broadhurst BR3 9DS		purchase order no 7721 date 14 04 20-X	
Product code	Quantity	Description	
EE8531	180	Enigma mats (chrome) less trade discount @ 15%	
AUTHORISED signature.......*T Gardner*........................date...*14/04/20-x*			

INVOICE

E Ragle Limited

56, Crown East Drive, Lower Broadhurst, BR3 9DS

Tel 01908 765321 Fax 01908 765977 Email sales@eragle.co.uk

VAT Reg GB 0745 4672 73

invoice to

W Walton Trading Ltd Unit 19 Mortella Business Park Broadfield BR3 7VB	invoice no 261857 account WW313 your reference 7721 date/tax point **19 April 20-X**

Product code	Description	Quantity	Price	Unit	Total	Discount @15%	Net
EE8531	Enigma mats (chrome)	180	9.75	each			

terms

Net monthly

Carriage paid

E & OE

Goods total	
VAT	
TOTAL	

(b) Enter the appropriate amounts from the completed invoice in Task 1 (a) in the sales day book shown below.

Sales day book

Date	Details	Invoice number	Total £	VAT £	Net £

(c)   A BACS payment for £2,758.10 has been received from Tristan Associates who incorrectly state that the amount is in full settlement of their account balance as at 30 June 20-X.

The customer's account in the sales ledger is shown below.

Dr   **Tristan Associates**   **Cr**

Date 20-X	Details	Amount £	Date 20-X	Details	Amount £
6 Jun	Balance b/f	2254.60	9 Jun	Credit note 241	120.00
13 Jun	Invoice 2436	250.00	17 Jun	Bank	750.00
16 Jun	Invoice 2476	1,280.00	14 Jun	Credit note 251	156.50
22 Jun	Invoice 2501	595.00	20 Jun	Credit note 260	98.00
27 Jun	Invoice 2534	55.00			

You are to calculate the correct up-to-date balance of the Tristan Associates account as shown in the sales ledger account above and then indicate with a tick in the right-hand column of the table below which three transactions are still outstanding.

Balance b/f	
Invoice 2436	
Invoice 2476	
Invoice 2501	
Invoice 2534	
Credit note 241	
Bank	
Credit note 251	
Credit note 260	

(d) E Ragle Limited has just introduced to its customers a prompt payment discount of 2% for payment within 10 days of the invoice date. M Tippit Ltd receives the invoice below and pays in full within 7 days. E Ragle Limited then sends a credit note to M Tippit for the amount to be refunded.

The total amount of the refund on the credit note (including VAT @ 20%) is £ ⬚

INVOICE

E Ragle Limited

56, Crown East Drive, Lower Broadhurst, BR3 9DS
Tel 01908 765321 Fax 01908 765977 Email sales@eragle.co.uk
VAT Reg GB 0745 4672 73

invoice to

M Tippit Ltd
25 Pound Bank Road
Hillfield
BR2 8ER

invoice no	261900
account	MT414
your reference	45426
date/tax point	30 June 20-X

Product code	Description	Quantity	Price	Unit	Total	20% trade discount	Net
EE2007	Celebration mugs	100	7.75	each	775.00	155.00	620.00

terms
Net monthly
Prompt payment discount of 2% for payment within 10 days
Carriage paid
E & OE

Goods total	620.00
VAT	124.00
TOTAL	744.00

Task 2

(a) The purchase order and invoice shown below relate to goods ordered and received by Sparkle Fashion Supplies. Compare the details on the two documents and answer the question on the next page.

Fashion First

10 High Street
Hereborough
HE6 9FG

PURCHASE ORDER

| Sparkle Fashion Supplies |
| Unit 3 Dugdale Way |
| Hereborough |
| HR4 8HG |

purchase order no   O2726
date   15 07 20-X

Product code	Quantity	Description
17634	25	Trend T Shirts (black) @ £10 less 20% trade discount

AUTHORISED   signature....... *J K Campbell* ....date....... *6/07/20-x*

INVOICE

Sparkle Fashion Supplies

Unit 3 Dugdale Way
Hereborough
HR4 8HG

invoice to

| Fashion First |
| 10 High Street |
| Hereborough |
| HE6 9FG |

invoice no   12793
account   FF309
your reference   O2627
date/tax point   18 July 20-X

Product code	Description	Quantity	Price	Unit	Total	Discount @20%	Net Total
17635	Trend T shirts (blue)	25	10.00	each	250.00	50.00	300.00

terms

Net monthly

Carriage paid

E & OE

Goods total	300.00
VAT	60.00
TOTAL	240.00

Task 2 (a) continued

Compare the purchase order and the invoice on the previous page.

Identify the discrepancies on the invoice and link the boxes below with lines. The left-hand column of boxes sets out where on the invoice errors could take place and the right-hand column of boxes describes the types of error that could occur.

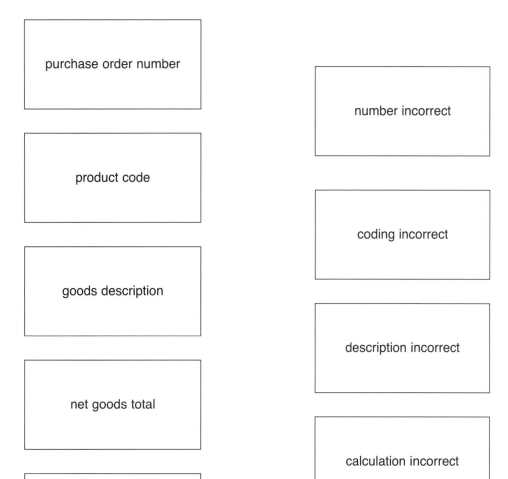

(b) The credit note shown below has been issued by Sparkle Fashion Supplies to Fashion First who have returned some damaged goods.

Record the details from the credit note in the appropriate day book operated by Sparkle Fashion Supplies. Choose between:

- Discounts allowed day book
- Discounts received day book
- Purchases day book
- Purchases returns day book
- Sales day book
- Sales returns day book

Name of day book:

Date 20-X	Details	Credit note number	Total £	VAT £	Net £

CREDIT NOTE

Sparkle Fashion Supplies

Unit 3 Dugdale Way
Hereborough
HR4 8HG

credit to

Fashion First
10 High Street
Hereborough
HE6 9FG

credit note no	2793
account	FF309
your reference	02700
date/tax point	25 July 20-X

Product code	Description	Quantity	Price	Unit	Total	Discount @20%	Net Total
186734	Rainbow scarves	5	15.00	each	75.00	15.00	60.00

reason for credit

Damaged goods returned

Goods total	60.00
VAT	12.00
TOTAL	72.00

Task 3

(a) 'Flash Guy' is an up-market clothes shop. The accountant always checks statements of account when they are received from suppliers. The statements have to be carefully checked because they may contain purchases which have not yet been received and recorded in Flash Guy's purchases ledger. Set out below are:

- the statement of account received from Trend Fashion Supplies Ltd.
- the supplier account of Trend Fashion Supplies Ltd in the purchases ledger of 'Flash Guy'

You are to:

- Compare the entries on the two documents to identify amounts which appear on only one of the documents.
- Tick the boxes next to the statement of account for the three items which are missing from the supplier account in the 'Flash Guy' purchases ledger and so should not be paid.

STATEMENT OF ACCOUNT

Trend Fashion Supplies Ltd
195 Camomile Street, London WC1 6FD

To Flash Guy
Date 31 Jan 20-X

Date 20-X	Invoice/credit note number	Details	Amount £	✔
5 Jan	INV1423	Goods	2,720	
10 Jan	INV1510	Goods	3,150	
19 Jan	INV1724	Goods	4,965	
22 Jan	CN872	Goods returned	495	
25 Jan	INV1792	Goods	1,789	
28 Jan	CN883	Goods returned	560	

Trend Fashion Supplies Ltd

Date 20-X	Details	Amount £	Date 20-X	Details	Amount £
8 Jan	Bank	8,760	5 Jan	Balance b/f	8,760
28 Jan	CN883	560	10 Jan	INV1510	3,150
			19 Jan	INV1724	4,965

(b)   The amount paid will be £ [   ]

(c)   Continental Paper plc has supplied Portsmouth Publishing with the wrong specification of paper. They have agreed to issue a credit note to provide a refund. Set out below are the account of Continental Paper plc in the purchases ledger of Portsmouth Publishing and the credit note issued. The credit note has not yet been entered into the purchases ledger account.

Continental Paper plc

Date 20-X	Details	Amount £	Date 20-X	Details	Amount £
1 Oct	Bank	12,500	1 Oct	Balance b/f	11,635
2 Oct	Credit note 753	3,600	4 Oct	Invoice 1810	12,250
			5 Oct	Invoice 1818	13,610
			8 Oct	Invoice 1824	2,645

CREDIT NOTE   **Continental Paper Plc**

Unit 12 Farnham Estate
Bath
BA1 5FG

credit to

Portsmouth Publishing		credit note no	4644
112 Dorset Road		account	PP170
Portsmouth		your reference	6251
PO9 6FG		date/tax point	12 October 20-X

Product code	Description	Quantity	Price	Unit	Total	Discount @10%	Net Total
P274	90gsm Fineblade (white) paper	40	245.00	100kg	9800.00	980.00	8820.00

reason for credit

Incorrect paper supplied - refund given

Goods total	8820.00
VAT	1764.00
TOTAL	10584.00

You are asked to calculate the amount that will be owing to Continental Paper plc by Portsmouth Publishing after the credit note has been entered into the the purchases ledger of Portsmouth Publishing.

The amount due is £

(d) The two invoices on this and the next page offer a prompt payment discount for settlement within a certain period of time indicated in the invoice terms.

INVOICE					No 1689		
HELICON OFFICE CLEANING					Date 10 04 20-X		
45 Dunster Street							
Mereford MR4 2DS							
VAT Reg 831 8627 06							
To							
Phillipson Training							
68 Whitecliff Street, Granstow, GR3 7GH							

Product code	Description	Quantity	Price	Unit	Total	Discount @20%	Net Total
OC235	Cleaning (1 week)	4	50.00	each	200.00	40.00	160.00

terms		
Net monthly	Goods total	160.00
Prompt payment discount of 5% for payment within 14 days of invoice date	VAT	32.00
E & OE	TOTAL	192.00

The amount that will be paid if the prompt payment discount is taken will be:

(a)	£182.40	
(b)	£172.80	
(c)	£160.00	

Tick the appropriate box.

The date by which the amount will have to be paid if the prompt payment discount is taken will be:

(a)	10 April	
(b)	24 April	
(c)	31 April	

Tick the appropriate box.

(d) continued

INVOICE					No 9262			
KEEPSAFE ALARMS SYSTEMS					**Date** 06 04 20-X			
190 Market Street								
Beresford BR1 2GH								
VAT Reg 831 8619 08								
To								
R Shah, Accountants								
93 High Street, Beresford, BE1 5IT								

Product code	Description	Quantity	Price	Unit	Total	Discount @10%	Net Total
AS616	Alarm system annual service	1	90.00	each	90.00	9.00	81.00

terms

Net monthly
Prompt payment discount of 4% for payment within 7 days
of invoice date
E & OE

Goods total	81.00
VAT	16.20
TOTAL	97.20

The amount that will be paid if the prompt payment discount is taken will be:

(a)	£97.20	
(b)	£93.96	
(c)	£93.31	

Tick the appropriate box.

The date by which the amount will have to be paid if the prompt payment discount is taken will be:

(a)	1 April	
(b)	13 April	
(c)	30 April	

Tick the appropriate box.

Task 4

The two amounts shown below have been received from customers and are ready to be entered in the cash book.

Watling Enterprises
Remittance advice
10 July 20-7
An amount of £1,240 will be transferred to your bank account today by BACS, in full settlement of our June account.

Receipt 263	10 July 20-7
Cheque for £500 and cash of £70 received from O'Hara & Co for goods supplied today.	
£570 including VAT.	

(a)   Make the necessary entries in the cash book and total each column.

Select your entries for the Details column from the following list: Bank, Cash, Cash purchases, O'Hara & Co, Trade payables, VAT, Watling Enterprises.

Cash book – debit side

Details	Cash	Bank	VAT	Trade receivables	Cash sales
	£	£	£	£	£
Balance b/f	156	2,369			
Totals					

(b)   The credit side of the cash book shows total cash payments during the week were £106.
Using your answers to (a), calculate the cash balance.

£

(c)   The credit side of the cash book shows total bank payments during the week were £6,278.
Using your answers to (a), calculate the bank balance. Use a minus sign if your calculations indicate an overdrawn bank balance, eg –123.

£ [   ]

Task 5

The two petty cash vouchers below are ready to be entered into the partially completed petty cash book.

petty cash voucher		233
date	*30 April 20-7*	

	£	p
Van repairs		
including VAT at 20%	*58*	*80*
Total	*58*	*80*

petty cash voucher		234
date	*30 April 20-7*	

	£	p
Postage stamps	*12*	*50*
VAT is not applicable		
	12	*50*

(a) Complete the petty cash book by:

• Entering both transactions into the petty cash book below.

Select your entry for the Details column from the following list: Balance b/f, Balance c/d, Envelopes, Office expenses, Postage stamps, VAT, Van repairs, Vehicle expenses.

• Totalling the petty cash book and inserting the balance carried down at 30 April.

Petty cash book

Date 20-7	Details	Amount £	Date 20-7	Details	Amount £	VAT £	Office expenses £	Vehicle expenses £
20 April	Balance b/f	68.18	20 April	Envelopes	6.72	1.12	5.60	
20 April	Cash from bank	81.82						
	Total			Totals				

(b) What will be the amount of cash withdrawn from the bank to restore the imprest level of £150.00?

£ _____

Task 6

These are the totals of the discounts received day book at the end of the month.

Discounts received day book

Details	Total £	VAT £	Net £
Totals	252	42	210

(a)   What will be the entries in the general ledger?

Select your account names from the following list: Discounts allowed, Discounts received, Purchases, Purchases ledger control, Purchases returns, Sales, Sales ledger control, Sales returns, VAT.

General ledger

Account name	Amount £	Debit	Credit

One of the entries in the discounts received day book is for a credit note received from Grover plc for £35 plus VAT.

(b)   What will be the entry in the purchases ledger?

Select your account name from the following list: Discounts allowed, Discounts received, Grover plc, Purchases, Purchases ledger control, Purchases returns, Sales, Sales ledger control, Sales returns, VAT.

Purchases ledger

Account name	Amount £	Debit	Credit

Task 7

These are the totals of the cash book at the end of the month.

Cash book

Cash £	Bank £	VAT £	Trade receivables £	Cash sales £	Cash £	Bank £	VAT £	Trade payables £	Cash purchases £
745	8,364	57	7,915	285	745	8,364	–	6,235	–

What will be the entries in the general ledger?

Select your account names from the following list: Bank, Cash, Cash purchases, Cash sales, Purchases ledger control, Sales ledger control, Trade payables, Trade receivables, VAT.

General ledger

Account name	Amount £	Debit	Credit

Task 8

The following two accounts are in the general ledger at close of day on 31 August.

Rent received

Date 20-7	Details	Amount £	Date 20-7	Details	Amount £
			1 Aug	Balance b/f	4,125
			26 Aug	Bank	895

Fixtures and fittings

Date 20-7	Details	Amount £	Date 20-7	Details	Amount £
1 Aug	Balance b/f	5,021	20 Aug	Journal	285
10 Aug	Bank	1,345			

(a)   What will be the balance brought down at 1 September on each account?

Account name	Balance b/d at 1 September £	Debit	Credit
Rent received			
Fixtures and fittings			

The following account is in the sales ledger at the close of day on 31 August.

(b)   Complete the account below by:

- Inserting the balance carried down together with date and details.
- Inserting the totals.
- Inserting the balance brought down together with date and details.

Christine Yeung

Date 20-7	Details	Amount £	Date 20-7	Details	Amount £
1 Aug	Balance b/f	2,156	5 Aug	Bank	1,376
20 Aug	Invoice 3986	1,084	10 Aug	Credit note CN541	115
	Total			Total	

Task 9

Below are two general ledger accounts and a partially completed trial balance.

Complete the trial balance by:

- Transferring the balances of the two general ledger accounts to the debit or credit column of the trial balance.

- Entering the amounts shown against each of the other account names into the debit or credit column of the trial balance.

- Totalling both columns of the trial balance.

Do not enter figures with decimal places in this task and do not enter a zero in unused column cells.

Sales returns

Date 20-7	Details	Amount £	Date 20-7	Details	Amount £
1 May	Balance b/f	1,325	10 May	Journal	110
31 May	Sales ledger control	854	31 May	Balance c/d	2,069
		2,179			2,179

Motor Vehicles

Date 20-7	Details	Amount £	Date 20-7	Details	Amount £
1 May	Balance b/f	52,100	10 May	Journal	1,385
15 May	Bank	8,590	31 May	Balance c/d	59,305
		60,690			60,690

Trial balance as at 31 May

Account name	Amount £	Debit £	Credit £
Sales returns			
Motor vehicles			
Bank (cash at bank)	2,285		
Loan from bank	10,350		
Purchases	45,365		
Sales	69,638		
Sales ledger control	12,821		
Purchases ledger control	7,117		
Rent and rates	5,260		
Capital	40,000		
Totals			

Task 10

A new business has allocated a code to seven new customer accounts in the sales ledger. The code is made up of the first four letters of the customer name, followed by the number of the ledger page. The ledger pages are set out in alphabetical order.

Customer name	Customer account code
Bryant Builders	BRYA02
Dixons Opticians	DIXO04
Hartley Accountants	HART08
James Wood & Co	JAME10
Owen Meats	OWEN15
Thompson Bookshop	THOM20
Warburton Petfood	WARB23

Two new customer accounts shown below have been added to the sales ledger and need to be allocated a customer account code.

(a) Insert the relevant account codes for each customer.

Account code [   ]

Pearson Art Studio

Date 20-X	Details	Amount £	Date 20-X	Details	Amount £
10 Oct	Invoice 7453	243			

Account code [   ]

Carrington Ltd

Date 20-X	Details	Amount £	Date 20-X	Details	Amount £
11 Oct	Invoice 7469	956			

Bryant Builders has been offered a prompt payment discount of 5% for payment of invoices within 10 days.

(b)   Indicate in the table below what **two** actions should be taken by the supplier if the customer takes the discount and pays within 10 days.

(a)	Record the amount received in the sales ledger	
(b)	Record the discount received in the purchases ledger	
(c)	Issue a credit note for the invoiced amount (excluding VAT)	
(d)	Issue a credit note for the discount amount (including VAT)	

A small business that manufactures picture frames has the following assets and liabilities.

Assets and liabilities	**£**
Manufacturing equipment	150,000
Vehicles	42,000
Inventories	25,100
Bank Loan	86,500
Trade receivables	29,760
Trade payables	18,210

(c)   Calculate the total assets and liabilities for the accounting equation and insert the appropriate figures below.

Assets £	**Liabilities £**	**Capital £**

(d)   The transactions set out below on the left have taken place within a travel company.

Decide whether each transaction will be classified as:

- capital income
- revenue income
- capital expenditure
- revenue expenditure

Draw a line between each transaction description on the left and the appropriate classification of income or expenditure set out on the right. You may need to use a classification more than once.

Holidays sold	CAPITAL INCOME
Sale of premises	
Insurance costs	CAPITAL EXPENDITURE
Purchase of new computer system	
Salaries and wages	REVENUE INCOME
Agents' commission	REVENUE EXPENDITURE

Practice assessment 3

This practice assessment contains 10 tasks and you should attempt to complete every task.

Each task is independent. You will not need to refer to your answers to previous tasks. Where the date is relevant, it is given in the task data.

The tasks are set in different business situations where the following apply:

- All businesses use a manual bookkeeping system.

- Double-entry takes place in the general ledger. Individual accounts of trade receivables and trade payables are kept in the sales and purchases ledgers as subsidiary accounts.

- The cash book and petty cash book should be treated as part of the double-entry system unless the task instructions state otherwise.

- The VAT rate is 20%.

Task 1

(a) You receive the purchase order shown below and are required to complete the following details on the invoice on the next page. The date is 25 October 20-X.

- the goods total before trade discount
- the discount amount
- the net amount after trade discount
- the VAT amount (VAT @ 20%)
- the invoice total

B Britten Domestics		**PURCHASE ORDER**
25, Grimes Park Road		
Broadfield		
BR1 8GH		

J T Avener Electrical 66 Athene Park Estate Hampstead London NW3 8GG	purchase order no date	**19867** **20 10 20-X**

Product code	Quantity	Description
28746	**95**	**MT Coffee machines, less trade discount @ 20%**

AUTHORISED   signature.........*N Marriner*...date....*20/10/20-x*......

J T AVENER ELECTRICAL

INVOICE

66, Athene Park Estate
Hampstead, London NW3 8GG
Tel 0207 765321 Fax 0207 765977 Email sales@jtavenerelectrical.com
VAT Reg GB 0745 4671 12

invoice to

| B Britten Domestics |
| 25, Grimes Park Road |
| Broadfield |
| BR1 8GH |

invoice no	2387
account	BD915
your reference	19867
date/tax point	25 October 20-X

Product code	Description	Quantity	Price	Unit	Total	Discount @20%	Net
28746	MT Coffee Machine	95	79.50	each			

terms

Net monthly

Carriage paid

E & OE

Goods total	
VAT	
TOTAL	

(b) Enter the appropriate amounts from the completed invoice in Task 1 (a) in the sales day book shown below.

Sales day book

Date	Details	Invoice number	Total £	VAT £	Net £

(c) A cheque payment for £1,217 has been received from La Tosca Restaurants who incorrectly state that the amount is in full settlement of their account balance as at 31 October 20-X.
The customer's account in the Sales Ledger is shown below.

Dr   **La Tosca Restaurants**   **Cr**

Date 20-X	Details	Amount £	Date 20-X	Details	Amount £
2 Oct	Balance b/f	1200.00	5 Oct	Bank	750.00
9 Oct	Invoice 1981	150.00	12 Oct	Credit note 471	78.00
16 Oct	Invoice 1990	790.00	18 Oct	Credit note 489	95.00
23 Oct	Invoice 2016	350.00	25 Oct	Credit note 501	67.00
30 Oct	Invoice 2032	200.00			

You are to calculate the correct up-to-date balance of the La Tosca Restaurants account as shown in the sales ledger account above and then indicate with a tick in the right-hand column of the table below which three transactions are still outstanding.

Balance b/f	
Invoice 1981	
Invoice 1990	
Invoice 2016	
Invoice 2032	
Bank	
Credit note 471	
Credit note 489	
Credit note 501	

(d)   Dormo Furniture Importers has just introduced to its customers a prompt payment discount of 5% for payment within 10 days of the invoice date. Rest Easy Bed Centre receives the invoice below and pays in full within 7 days. Dormo Furniture Importers then sends a credit note to Rest Easy Bed Centre for the amount to be refunded.

The total amount of the refund on the credit note (including VAT @ 20%) is £ [   ]

INVOICE

Dormo Furniture Importers

Unit 12, Blackberry Estate, Worcester WR3 9DZ
Tel 0190 748221 Fax 0190 748222 Email sales@dormofurniture.co.uk
VAT Reg GB 0777 4634 78

invoice to

Rest Easy Bed Centre
49 Link Road
Bradland
WR2 5HD

invoice no	8141
account	RE332
your reference	97941
date/tax point	27 October 20-X

Product code	Description	Quantity	Price	Unit	Total	20% trade discount	Net
VS1091	Snoozer 5ft bed	5	895.00	each	4475.00	895.00	3580.00

terms
Net monthly
Prompt payment discount of 5% for payment within 10 days
Carriage paid
E & OE

Goods total	3580.00
VAT	716.00
TOTAL	4296.00

Task 2

(a)   The purchase order and invoice shown below relate to goods ordered and received by Albinoni Italian Restaurant. Compare the details on the two documents and answer the question on the next page.

Albinoni Italian Restaurant

75 Archway Hill
London
N19 5NF

PURCHASE ORDER

Pasta World	purchase order no	**10967**
45 St Margarets Avenue	date	**25 07 20-X**
St Margarets		
London TW1 2LH		

Product code	Quantity	Description
94924	**50 packs**	**Ravioli (ricotta e spinaci) @ £1.20 per pack with 20% trade discount**

AUTHORISED   signature..........*H Caruso*......................................date..*25/07/20-x*......

INVOICE   **Pasta World**

45 St Margarets Avenue
St Margarets
London TW1 2LH

invoice to

Albinoni Italian Restaurant	invoice no	9826
75 Archway Hill	account	1402
London	your reference	10976
N19 5NF	date/tax point	28 July 20-x

Product code	Description	Quantity	Price	Unit	Total	Discount	Net
92924	Ravioli (ricotta e spinaci)	60	1.20	pack	72.00	none	72.00

terms

Net monthly

Carriage paid

E & OE

Goods total	72.00
VAT	14.40
TOTAL	86.00

Task 2 (a) continued

Compare the purchase order and the invoice on the previous page.

Identify the discrepancies on the invoice and link the boxes below with lines. The left-hand column of boxes sets out where on the invoice errors could take place and the right-hand column of boxes describes the types of error that could occur.

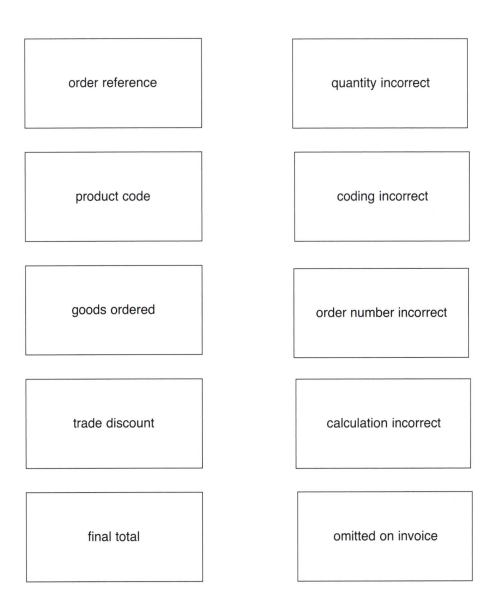

order reference

quantity incorrect

product code

coding incorrect

goods ordered

order number incorrect

trade discount

calculation incorrect

final total

omitted on invoice

Task 2

(b) The invoice shown at the bottom of the page has been received by Albinoni Italian Restaurant.

Record the details from the invoice in the appropriate day book operated by Albinoni Italian Restaurant. Choose between:

- Discounts allowed day book
- Discounts received day book
- Purchases day book
- Purchases returns day book
- Sales day book
- Sales returns day book

Name of day book:					
Date 20-X	Details	Invoice number	Total £	VAT £	Net £

INVOICE	**Pasta World**

45 St Margarets Avenue
St Margarets
London TW1 2LH

invoice to

Albinoni Italian Restaurant 75 Archway Hill London N19 5NF	invoice no	9826
	account	1402
	your reference	10976
	date/tax point	28 July 20-X

Product code	Description	Quantity	Price £	Unit	Total £	Discount @ 20% £	Net £
92924	Spaghetti (fresh)	15	20.00	pack	300.00	60.00	240.00

terms
Net monthly
Carriage paid
E & OE

Goods total	240.00
VAT	48.00
TOTAL	288.00

Task 3

(a) Dogs4U always checks statements of account when they are received from suppliers. The statements have to be carefully checked because they may contain purchases which have not yet been received and recorded in Dogs4U's purchases ledger. Set out below are:

- the statement of account received from Petfood Supplies Ltd
- the supplier account of Petfood Supplies Ltd in the purchases ledger of Dogs4U

You are to:

- Compare the entries on the two documents to identify amounts which appear on only one of the documents.

- Tick the boxes next to the statement of account for the three items which are missing from the supplier account in Dogs4U's purchases ledger and so should not be paid.

STATEMENT OF ACCOUNT
Petfood Supplies Ltd
34, Cavalier Street, Mereford MR1 7TY

To Dogs4U
Date 31 10 20-X

Date 20-X	Invoice/credit note number	Details	Amount £	✔
1 Oct	INV945	Goods	1,950	
8 Oct	INV956	Goods	420	
15 Oct	CN181	Goods returned	250	
22 Oct	INV972	Goods	2,720	
25 Oct	CN198	Goods returned	649	
31 Oct	INV995	Goods	1,760	

Petfood Supplies Ltd

Date 20-X	Details	Amount £	Date 20-X	Details	Amount £
5 Oct	Bank	3,750	1 Oct	Balance b/f	3,750
15 Oct	CN181	250	1 Oct	INV945	1,950
			22 Oct	INV972	2,720

(b) The amount paid will be £ [   ]

(c) Excelsior Sports Equipment supplies Kingsworthy School with a variety of sports goods. The school's accountant has been off sick for all of April and a number of invoices received from Excelsior Sports Equipment have been ignored with the result that Excelsior Sports Equipment has been sending out chasers to the school to ask for the funds.

The last letter (dated 30 April) sent to the school contained copies of four invoices and a schedule listing them. The schedule is shown below:

Excelsior Sports Equipment

Schedule of unpaid invoices for April 20-X due by 30 April (including VAT).

1	Invoice 9817 for rugby equipment	£550.90
2	Invoice 9834 for hockey equipment	£675.00
3	Invoice 9856 for football equipment	£220.00
4	Invoice 9867 for cricket equipment	£640.50

Please pay by BACS transfer to Lloyds Bank Kingworth

Account details: Excelsior Sports Equipment
30 56 99 (sortcode) 82425903 (account number)

Signed: S C Rouge (Chief Accountant)

Excelsior Sports Equipment

Date 20-X	Details	Amount £	Date 20-X	Details	Amount £
1 Apr	Bank	1857.00	1 Apr	Balance b/f	1857.00
12 Apr	Credit note 753	275.50			

The amount that will be owing to Excelsior Sports Equipment by Kingsworthy School after taking into account the four missing invoices is:

£ [   ]

(d) The two invoices on this and the next page offer a prompt payment discount for settlement within a certain period of time indicated in the invoice terms.

INVOICE

No 1689

STAYSAFE INSURANCE BROKERS

Date 08 07 20-X

91 Spicer Street
Mereford MR2 9QP
VAT Reg 107 8627 33

To
T T Ripov Payroll Services
68 Whitecliff Street, Granstow, GR3 7GH

Product code	Description	Quantity	Price	Unit	Total	Discount @20%	Net Total
P717	June payroll processing	1	120.00	each	120.00	24.00	96.00

terms

Net monthly
Prompt payment discount of 5% for payment within 7 days
of invoice date
E & OE

Goods total	96.00
VAT	19.20
TOTAL	115.20

The amount that will be paid if the prompt payment discount is taken will be:

(a)	£109.44	
(b)	£115.20	
(c)	£107.14	

Tick the appropriate box.

The date by which the amount will have to be paid if the prompt payment discount is taken will be:

(a)	13 July	
(b)	15 July	
(c)	20 July	

Tick the appropriate box.

(d) continued

INVOICE					No 7825		

Reuben's Paint Supplies
115 Market Street
Beresford BR1 2GH
VAT Reg 831 6271 13

Date 06 07 20-X

To
Woodrow Designs
23 High Street, Cooperfield, CP1 5IT

Product code	Description	Quantity	Price	Unit	Total	Discount @20%	Net Total
6551	Crownex matt emulsion (cream)	40	12.00	Tins 5lt	480.00	96.00	384.00

terms

Net monthly
Prompt payment discount of 2.5% for payment within 14
days of invoice date
E & OE

Goods total	384.00
VAT	76.80
TOTAL	460.80

The amount that will be paid if the prompt payment discount is taken will be:

(a)	£460.80	
(b)	£449.28	
(c)	£472.32	

Tick the appropriate box.

The date by which the amount will have to be paid if the prompt payment discount is taken will be:

(a)	20 July	
(b)	21 July	
(c)	31 July	

Tick the appropriate box.

Task 4

The two amounts shown below have been received from customers and are ready to be entered in the cash book.

Albion Supplies
Remittance advice
12 May 20-8
An amount of £1,089 will be transferred to your bank account today by BACS, in full settlement of our April account.

Receipt 456	12 May 20-8
Cheque for £250 and cash of £62 received from Dalton Ltd for goods supplied today. £312 including VAT.	

(a)   Make the necessary entries in the cash book and total each column.

Select your entries for the Details column from the following list: Albion Supplies, Bank, Cash, Cash purchases, Dalton Ltd, Trade payables, VAT.

Cash book – debit side

Details	Cash £	Bank £	VAT £	Trade receivables £	Cash sales £
Balance b/f	135	1,362			
Totals					

(b)   The credit side of the cash book shows total cash payments during the week were £148.

Using your answers to (a), calculate the cash balance.

£ [   ]

(c)   The credit side of the cash book shows total bank payments during the week were £1,852.

Using your answers to (a), calculate the bank balance. Use a minus sign if your calculations indicate an overdrawn bank balance, eg −123.

£ [   ]

Task 5

The two petty cash vouchers below are ready to be entered into the partially completed petty cash book.

petty cash voucher		272
date *31 May 20-8*		

	£	p
Photocopier supplies	*15*	*50*
VAT at 20%	*3*	*10*
Total	*18*	*60*

petty cash voucher		273
date *31 May 20-8*		

	£	p
Rail fare	*20*	*50*
VAT is not applicable		
	20	*50*

(a) Complete the petty cash book by:

• Entering both transactions into the petty cash book below.

Select your entry for the Details column from the following list: Balance b/f, Balance c/d, Office expenses, Photocopier, Rail fare, Travel expenses, VAT.

• Totalling the petty cash book and inserting the balance carried down at 31 May.

Petty cash book

Date 20-8	Details	Amount £	Date 20-8	Details	Amount £	VAT £	Office expenses £	Travel expenses £
10 May	Balance b/f	154.90	17 May	Pencils	6.72	1.12	5.60	
10 May	Cash from bank	45.10						
	Total			Totals				

(b) What will be the amount of cash withdrawn from the bank to restore the imprest level of £200.00?

£ _____

Task 6

These are the totals of the discounts allowed day book at the end of the month.

Discounts allowed day book

Details	Total £	VAT £	Net £
Totals	156	26	130

(a) What will be the entries in the general ledger?

Select your account names from the following list: Discounts allowed, Discounts received, Purchases, Purchases ledger control, Purchases returns, Sales, Sales ledger control, Sales returns, VAT.

General ledger

Account name	Amount £	Debit	Credit

One of the entries in the discounts allowed day book is for a credit note sent to Groves Ltd for £45 plus VAT.

(b) What will be the entry in the sales ledger?

Select your account name from the following list: Discounts allowed, Discounts received, Groves Ltd, Purchases, Purchases ledger control, Purchases returns, Sales, Sales ledger control, Sales returns, VAT.

Sales ledger

Account name	Amount £	Debit	Credit

Task 7

These are the totals of the cash book at the end of the month.

Cash book

Cash £	Bank £	VAT £	Trade receivables £	Cash sales £	Cash £	Bank £	VAT £	Trade payables £	Cash purchases £
540	6,105	–	5,829	–	540	6,105	37	4,322	185

What will be the entries in the general ledger?

Select your account names from the following list: Bank, Cash, Cash purchases, Cash sales, Purchases ledger control, Sales ledger control, Trade payables, Trade receivables, VAT.

General ledger

Account name	Amount £	Debit	Credit

Task 8

The following two accounts are in the general ledger at close of day on 31 October.

Capital

Date 20-8	Details	Amount £	Date 20-8	Details	Amount £
			1 Oct	Balance b/f	24,200
			15 Oct	Bank	5,150

Office equipment

Date 20-8	Details	Amount £	Date 20-8	Details	Amount £
1 Oct	Balance b/f	10,220	28 Oct	Journal	265
20 Oct	Bank	2,195			

(a) What will be the balance brought down at 1 November on each account?

Account name	Balance b/d at 1 November £	Debit	Credit
Capital			
Office equipment			

The following account is in the purchases ledger at the close of day on 31 October.

(b) Complete the account below by:

- Inserting the balance carried down together with date and details.
- Inserting the totals.
- Inserting the balance brought down together with date and details.

Olivia Kelly

Date 20-8	Details	Amount £	Date 20-8	Details	Amount £
22 Oct	Bank	2,741	1 Oct	Balance b/f	3,914
28 Oct	Credit note CN457	318	20 Oct	Invoice 2659	1,216
	Total			Total	

Task 9

Below are two general ledger accounts and a partially completed trial balance.

Complete the trial balance by:

- Transferring the balances of the two general ledger accounts to the debit or credit column of the trial balance.

- Entering the amounts shown against each of the other account names into the debit or credit column of the trial balance.

- Totalling both columns of the trial balance.

Do not enter figures with decimal places in this task and do not enter a zero in unused column cells.

Purchases

Date 20-8	Details	Amount £	Date 20-8	Details	Amount £
1 Feb	Balance b/f	25,085	14 Feb	Journal	275
28 Feb	Purchases ledger control	9,026	28 Feb	Balance c/d	33,836
		34,111			34,111

Office equipment

Date 20-8	Details	Amount £	Date 20-8	Details	Amount £
1 Feb	Balance b/f	12,250	20 Feb	Journal	850
16 Feb	Bank	1,650	28 Feb	Balance c/d	13,050
		13,900			13,900

Trial balance as at 28 February

Account name	Amount £	Debit £	Credit £
Purchases			
Office equipment			
Administration expenses	6,105		
Bank (overdraft)	3,211		
Motor vehicles	25,250		
Sales	58,582		
Sales ledger control	17,287		
Purchases ledger control	11,096		
Wages	22,361		
Capital	45,000		
Totals			

Task 10

A new business has allocated a code to seven new customer accounts in the sales ledger. The code is made up of the first four letters of the customer name, followed by the number of the ledger page. The ledger pages are set out in alphabetical order.

Customer name	Customer account code
Cotton Ltd	COTT03
Evans & Co	EVAN05
Hope Ltd	HOPE08
Kirk Builders Ltd	KIRK11
Johnston Antiques	JOHN10
Sinclair Optics Ltd	SINC19
Whitelaw Ltd	WHIT23

Two new customer accounts shown below have been added to the sales ledger and need to be allocated a customer account code.

(a) Insert the relevant account codes for each customer.

Fournier Music Ltd   Account code

Date 20-X	Details	Amount £	Date 20-X	Details	Amount £
19 Apr	Invoice 1307	65			

Copland Kitchen Design   Account code

Date 20-X	Details	Amount £	Date 20-X	Details	Amount £
19 Apr	Invoice 1308	625			

Your business has been offered by a supplier a prompt payment discount of 4% for payment of invoices within 10 days.

(b)   Indicate in the table below what **two** actions should be taken by you if you take the discount and pay within 10 days.

(a)	Record the amount paid to the supplier in the cash book and ledgers	
(b)	Change the total on the invoice to take the discount into account	
(c)	Deduct the discount from the payment, including the VAT due	
(d)	Deduct the discount from the payment but pay the full VAT amount	

A small business that manufactures picture frames has the following assets and liabilities.

Assets and liabilities	£
Property	250,000
Trade receivables	7,610
Inventories	8,170
Bank Loan	110,000
Bank overdraft	6,950
Trade payables	5,930

(c)   Calculate the total assets and liabilities for the accounting equation and insert the appropriate figures below.

Assets £	Liabilities £	Capital £

(d)   The transactions set out below on the left have taken place within a manufacturing company.

Decide whether each transaction will be classified as:

- capital income

- revenue income

- capital expenditure

- revenue expenditure

Draw a line between each transaction description on the left and the appropriate classification of income or expenditure set out on the right. You may need to use a classification more than once.

Sale of machinery	CAPITAL INCOME
Sales of manufactured goods	
Insurance premium	CAPITAL EXPENDITURE
Wages	REVENUE INCOME
Purchase of computer	
Clients' fees received	REVENUE EXPENDITURE

Answers to practice assessment 1

Task 1

(a)

```
━━━━━━━━━━━━━━ INVOICE ━━━━━━━━━━━━━━
                J Bark Trading Limited
              35 High Road, Wonsbury, WO6 5FG
     Tel 01908 765314  Fax 01908 765951  Email sales@barkertrading.co.uk
                   VAT Reg GB 0745 4672 76
```

invoice to

G Finsey Limited		invoice no	787923
Unit 23 Broadfield Estate		account	3993
Broadfield		your reference	47609
BR6 8YU		date/tax point	13 May 20-X

Product code	Description	Quantity	Price	Unit	Total	Discount @10%	Net
36119	30mm Blue grinder	150	1.50	each	225.00	22.50	202.50

terms
Net monthly
Carriage paid
E & OE

Goods total	202.50
VAT	40.50
TOTAL	243.00

(b)   **Sales day book**

Date	Details	Invoice number	Total £	VAT £	Net £
13 May	G Finsey Limited	787923	243.00	40.50	202.50

(c)

Balance b/f	
Credit note 755	
Bank	
Invoice 3431	
Invoice 3478	
Credit note 761	
Invoice 3493	✔
Credit note 769	✔
Invoice 3510	✔

(d)   £12.46 (rounded up)

Task 2 (a)

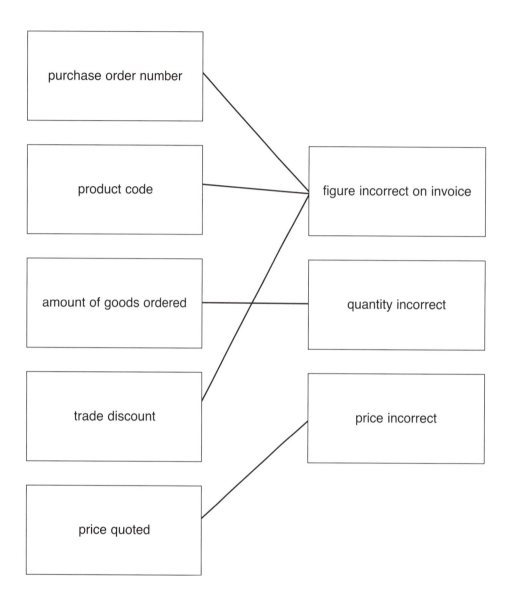

(b)

Name of day book: Sales day book					
Date 20-X	**Details**	**Invoice** **number**	**Total** £	**VAT** £	**Net** £
25 Jul	James Plant Garden Centre	787963	108.00	18.00	90.00

Task 3 (a)

STATEMENT OF ACCOUNT			To Lumino Lighting	
Sparks Electrical supplies			Date 30 06 20-X	
45 Jarvis Street, Mereford MR1 2GH				

Date 20-X	Invoice/credit note number	Details	Amount £	
1 Jul	CN1073	Goods returned	200	
8 Jul	INV1780	Goods	590	✔
14 Jul	INV1810	Goods	10,250	
21 Jul	CN1090	Goods returned	195	✔
24 Jul	INV1975	Goods	1,720	
30 Jul	INV2006	Goods	710	✔

(b) The amount paid will be £ | 11,770 |

(c) The amount due is £ | 6,696 |

(d)   (c)   Invoice 1: £470.40 by (c) 20 August
          (b)   Invoice 2: £307.80 by (a) 16 August

Task 4

(a) Cash book – credit side

Details	Cash £	Bank £	VAT £	Trade payables £	Cash purchases £
Balance b/f		4,720			
Alvington Supplies	180		30		150
Halwell Ltd		2,106		2,106	
Frogmore & Co		1,164		1,164	
Totals	180	7,990	30	3,270	150

(b) £482

(c) £–2,649

Task 5

(a)

Petty cash book

Date 20-6	Details	Amount £	Date 20-6	Details	Amount £	VAT £	Office expenses £	Cleaning £
15 June	Balance b/f	47.80	20 June	Postage stamps	40.00		40.00	
15 June	Cash from bank	77.20	30 June	Paper	24.00	4.00	20.00	
			30 June	Window cleaning	10.00			10.00
			30 June	Balance c/d	51.00			
	Total	125.00		**Totals**	125.00	4.00	60.00	10.00

(b) £74.00

Task 6

(a)   **General ledger**

Account name	Amount £	Debit	Credit
Discounts allowed	320	✔	
VAT	64	✔	
Sales ledger control	384		✔

(b)   **Sales ledger**

Account name	Amount £	Debit	Credit
Modbury Ltd	78		✔

Task 7

(a)   **General ledger**

Account name	Amount £	Debit	Credit
VAT	51	✔	
Purchases ledger control	9,105	✔	
Cash purchases	255	✔	
Sales ledger control	12,790		✔

Task 8

(a)

Account name	Balance b/d at 1 October £	Debit	Credit
Loan from bank	24,855		✔
Motor vehicles	22,030	✔	

(b)

Thomas Thomson

Date 20-6	Details	Amount £	Date 20-6	Details	Amount £
20 Sep	Bank	3,089	1 Sep	Balance b/f	6,241
25 Sep	Credit note C459	547	15 Sep	Invoice 4731	1,468
30 Sep	Balance c/d	4,073			
	Total	7,709		Total	7,709
			1 Oct	Balance b/d	4,073

Task 9

Trial balance as at 30 April

Account name	Amount £	Debit £	Credit £
Sales			79,085
Purchases		40,029	
Administration expenses	4,351	4,351	
Loan from bank	6,400		6,400
Office equipment	15,050	15,050	
Selling expenses	4,965	4,965	
Sales ledger control	18,273	18,273	
Purchases ledger control	12,692		12,692
Wages	28,518	28,518	
Capital	13,009		13,009
Totals		111,186	111,186

Task 10

(a)   WESL23, SANS19

(b)   (a)   Record the amount received in the cash book and ledgers

             (d)   Issue a credit note for the discount taken (including VAT)

(c)   Total assets £224,630 minus total liabilities £43,037 = Capital £181,593

(d)

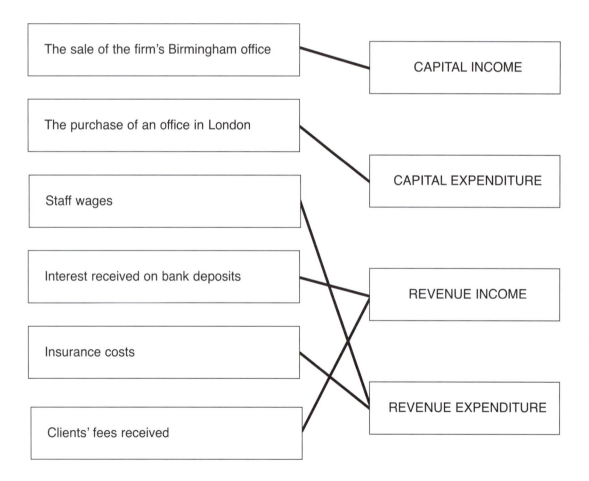

Answers to practice assessment 2

Task 1

(a)

```
━━━━━━━━━━━━━━━━ ● INVOICE ● ━━━━━━━━━━━━━━━━
                        E Ragle Limited
          56, Crown East Drive, Lower Broadhurst, BR3 9DS
          Tel 01908 765321  Fax 01908 765977  Email sales@eragle.co.uk
                     VAT Reg GB 0745 4672 73
```

invoice to

W Walton Trading Ltd Unit 19 Mortella Business Park Broadfield BR3 7VB		invoice no	261857
		account	WW313
		your reference	7721
		date/tax point	19 April 20-X

Product code	Description	Quantity	Price	Unit	Total	Discount @15%	Net
EE8531	Enigma mats (chrome)	180	9.75	each	1755.00	263.25	1491.75

terms
Net monthly
Carriage paid
E & OE

Goods total	1491.75
VAT	298.35
TOTAL	1790.10

(b) **Sales day book**

Date	Details	Invoice number	Total £	VAT £	Net £
19 Apr	W Walton Trading Ltd	261857	1790.10	298.35	1491.75

(c)

Balance b/f	
Invoice 2436	
Invoice 2476	
Invoice 2501	✔
Invoice 2534	✔
Credit note 241	
Bank	
Credit note 251	
Credit note 260	✔

(d)   £14.88

Task 2 (a)

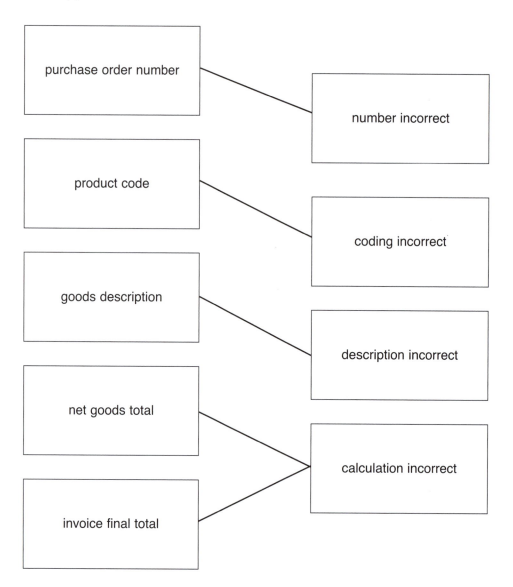

(b)

Name of day book: Sales returns day book					
Date 20-X	Details	Credit note number	Total £	VAT £	Net £
25 Jul	Fashion First	2793	72.00	12.00	60.00

Task 3 (a)

Date 20-X	Invoice/credit note number	Details	Amount £	
5 Jan	INV1423	Goods	2720	✔
10 Jan	INV1510	Goods	3150	
19 Jan	INV1724	Goods	4965	
22 Jan	CN872	Goods returned	495	✔
25 Jan	INV1792	Goods	1,789	✔
28 Jan	CN883	Goods returned	560	

STATEMENT OF ACCOUNT
Trend Fashion Supplies Ltd
195 Camomile Street, London WC1 6FD

To Flash Guy
Date 31 Jan 20-X

(b) The amount paid will be: £ 7,555

(c) The amount due is: £ 13,456

(d) Invoice 1: (a) £182.40 by (b) 24 April

Invoice 2: (c) £93.31 by (b) 13 April

Task 4

(a) Cash book – debit side

Details	Cash	Bank	VAT	Trade receivables	Cash sales
	£	£	£	£	£
Balance b/f	156	2,369			
Watling Enterprises		1,240		1,240	
O'Hara & Co	70	500	95		475
Totals	226	4,109	95	1,240	475

(b) £120

(c) £–2,169

Task 5

(a)

Petty cash book

Date 20-7	Details	Amount	Date 20-7	Details	Amount	VAT	Office expenses	Vehicle expenses
		£			£	£	£	£
20 April	Balance b/f	68.18	20 April	Envelopes	6.72	1.12	5.60	
20 April	Cash from bank	81.82	30 April	Van repairs	58.80	9.80		49.00
			30 April	Postage stamps	12.50		12.50	
			30 April	Balance c/d	71.98			
	Total	150.00		Totals	150.00	10.92	18.10	49.00

(b) £78.02

Task 6

(a)   General ledger

Account name	Amount £	Debit	Credit
Discounts received	210		✔
VAT	42		✔
Purchases ledger control	252	✔	

(b)   Purchases ledger

Account name	Amount £	Debit	Credit
Grover plc	42	✔	

Task 7

(a)   General ledger

Account name	Amount £	Debit	Credit
VAT	57		✔
Purchases ledger control	6,235	✔	
Cash sales	285		✔
Sales ledger control	7,915		✔

Task 8

(a)

Account name	Balance b/d at 1 September £	Debit	Credit
Rent received	5,020		✔
Fixtures and fittings	6,081	✔	

(b)

Christine Yeung

Date 20-7	Details	Amount £	Date 20-7	Details	Amount £
1 Aug	Balance b/f	2,156	5 Aug	Bank	1,376
20 Aug	Invoice 3986	1,084	10 Aug	Credit note CN541	115
			31 Aug	Balance c/d	1,749
	Total	3,240		Total	3,240
1 Sep	Balance b/d	1,749			

Task 9

Trial balance as at 31 May

Account name	Amount £	Debit £	Credit £
Sales returns		2,069	
Motor vehicles		59,305	
Bank (cash at bank)	2,285	2,285	
Loan from bank	10,350		10,350
Purchases	45,365	45,365	
Sales	69,638		69,638
Sales ledger control	12,821	12,821	
Purchases ledger control	7,117		7,117
Rent and rates	5,260	5,260	
Capital	40,000		40,000
Totals		127,105	127,105

Task 10

(a) PEAR16, CARR03

(b) (a) Record the amount received in the sales ledger

(d) Issue a credit note for the discount amount (including VAT)

(c) Total assets £246,860 minus total liabilities £104,710 = Capital £142,150

(d)

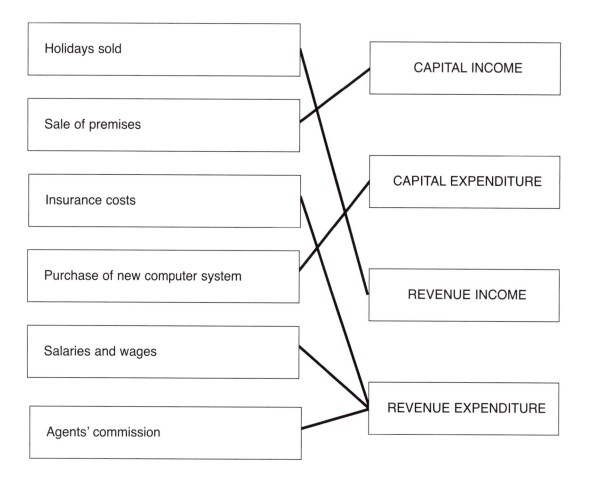

Answers to practice assessment 3

Task 1

(a)

J T AVENER ELECTRICAL   INVOICE

66, Athene Park Estate
Hampstead, London NW3 8GG
Tel 0207 765321 Fax 0207 765977 Email sales@jtavenerelectrical.com
VAT Reg GB 0745 4671 12

invoice to

B Britten Domestics 25, Grimes Park Road Broadfield BR1 8GH		invoice no	2387
		account	BD915
		your reference	19867
		date/tax point	25 Osctober 20-X

Product code	Description	Quantity	Price	Unit	Total	Discount @20%	Net
28746	MT Coffee Machine	95	79.50	each	7552.50	1510.50	6042.00

terms
Net monthly
Carriage paid
E & OE

Goods total	6042.00
VAT	1208.40
TOTAL	7250.40

(b)   **Sales day book**

Date	Details	Invoice number	Total £	VAT £	Net £
25 Oct	B Britten Domestics	2387	7250.40	1208.40	6042.00

(c)

Balance b/f	
Invoice 1981	
Invoice 1990	
Invoice 2016	✔
Invoice 2032	✔
Bank	
Credit note 471	
Credit note 489	
Credit note 501	✔

(d)   £214.80

Task 2 (a)

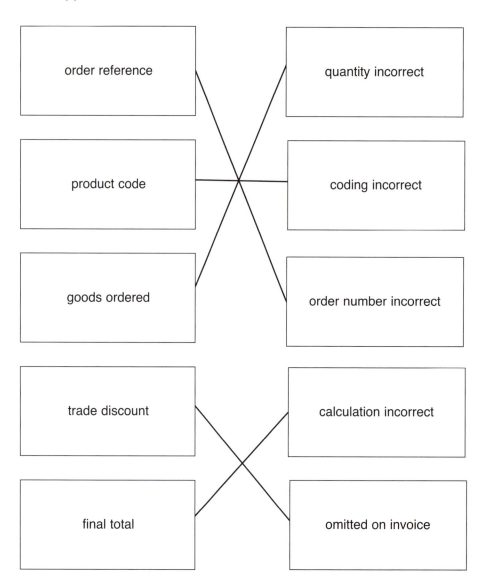

Task 2 (b)

Name of day book: Purchases day book					
Date 20-X	Details	Invoice number	Total £	VAT £	Net £
28 July	Pasta World	9826	288.00	48.00	240.00

Task 3 (a)

STATEMENT OF ACCOUNT					
Petfood Supplies Ltd 34, Cavalier Street, Mereford MR1 7TY			**To** Dogs4U **Date** 31 10 20-X		
Date 20-X	**Invoice/credit note** **number**	**Details**	**Amount** **£**		
1 Oct	INV945	Goods	1950		
8 Oct	INV956	Goods	420		✔
15 Oct	CN181	Goods returned	250		
22 Oct	INV972	Goods	2,720		
25 Oct	CN198	Goods returned	649		✔
31 Oct	INV995	Goods	1,760		✔

(b)   The amount paid will be: £ 4,420

(c)   The amount owing is: £ 1,810.90

(d)   Invoice 1: (a) 109.44 by (b) 15 July

Invoice 2: (b) £449.28 by (a) 20 July

Task 4

(a) Cash book – debit side

Details	Cash £	Bank £	VAT £	Trade receivables £	Cash sales £
Balance b/f	135	1,362			
Albion Supplies		1,089		1,089	
Dalton Ltd	62	250	52		260
Totals	197	2,701	52	1,089	260

(b) £49

(c) £849

Task 5

(a)

Petty cash book

Date 20-8	Details	Amount £	Date 20-8	Details	Amount £	VAT £	Office expenses £	Travel expenses £
10 May	Balance b/f	154.90	17 May	Pencils	6.72	1.12	5.60	
10 May	Cash from bank	45.10	31 May	Photocopier	18.60	3.10	15.50	
			31 May	Rail fare	20.50			20.50
			31 May	Balance c/d	154.18			
	Total	200.00		Totals	200.00	4.22	21.10	20.50

(b) £45.82

Task 6

(a)   General ledger

Account name	Amount £	Debit	Credit
Discounts allowed	130	✔	
VAT	26	✔	
Sales ledger control	156		✔

(b)   Sales ledger

Account name	Amount £	Debit	Credit
Groves plc	54		✔

Task 7

(a)   General ledger

Account name	Amount £	Debit	Credit
VAT	37	✔	
Purchases ledger control	4,322	✔	
Cash purchases	185	✔	
Sales ledger control	5,829		✔

Account name	Balance b/d at 1 November £	Debit	Credit
Capital	29,350		✔
Office equipment	12,150	✔	

ivia Kelly

Date 20-8	Details	Amount £	Date 20-8	Details	Amount £
22 Oct	Bank	2,741	1 Oct	Balance b/f	3,914
28 Oct	Credit note CN457	318	20 Oct	Invoice 2659	1,216
31 Oct	Balance c/d	2,071			
	Total	5,130		Total	5,130
			1 Nov	Balance b/d	2,071

Task 9

Trial balance as at 28 February

Account name	Amount £	Debit £	Credit £
Purchases		33,836	
Office equipment		13,050	
Administration expenses	6,105	6,105	
Bank (overdraft)	3,211		3,211
Motor vehicles	25,250	25,250	
Sales	58,582		58,582
Sales ledger control	17,287	17,287	
Purchases ledger control	11,096		11,096
Wages	22,361	22,361	
Capital	45,000		45,000
Totals		117,889	117,889

Task 10

(a)   FOUR06, COPL03

(b)   (a)   Record the amount paid to the supplier in the cash book and ledgers

(c)   Deduct the discount from the payment, including the VAT due

(c)   Total assets £265,780 minus total liabilities £122,880 = Capital £142,900

(d)

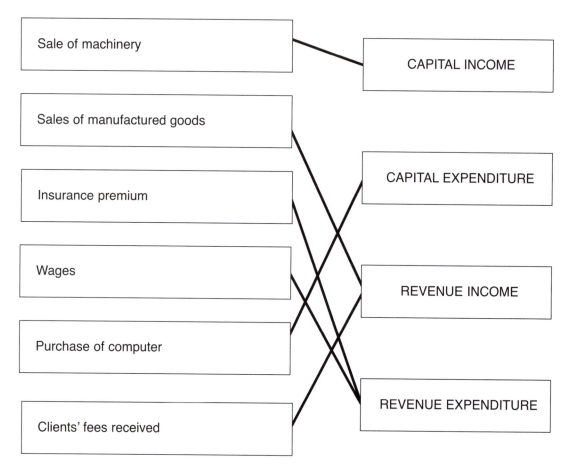

for your notes

for your notes

for your notes

for your notes

for your notes

for your notes

for your notes

for your notes